HOW TO SUCCEED
WITH
iQ
TESTS

KEN RUSSELL AND PHILIP CARTER

CAXTON EDITIONS

First Published in 1997
This edition published in 2000
by Caxton Editions
a member of the Caxton Publishing Group
20 Bloomsbury Street, London, WC1B 3QA

Designed by K Design, Winscombe, Somerset
Typeset by Keystroke, Jacaranda Lodge, Wolverhampton
Cover design for this edition by Open Door Limited
Printed in Great Britain by WBC Book Manufacturers Ltd

British Library Cataloguing in Publication Data

Title: How to Succeed with IQ Tests
ISBN: 1 84067 040 1

CONTENTS

Introduction

WHAT IS INTELLIGENCE?

Intelligence is the capacity to learn or understand. It is the ability of mind which varies in amount from person to person, but for any individual remains the same throughout life.

WHAT IS IQ?

The letters 'IQ' stand for 'Intelligence Quotient'. The definition of intelligence is the ability to 'comprehend quickly'; and quotient is the number of times that one number will divide into another. When measuring the IQ of a child, the subject would be asked to attempt an intelligence test which had been given to thousands of children and the results correlated so that the average score had been assessed for each age group. Thus, a child who at eight years of age obtained a result expected of a ten-year-old would score an IQ of 125 by the following calculation:

$$\frac{\text{Mental age}}{\text{chronological age}} \times 100 = \text{IQ}$$

$$\text{Therefore: } \frac{10}{8} \times 100 = 125 \text{ IQ}$$

A child of eight years of age who successfully passed a test for a child of eight but failed a test for a child of nine years would have an IQ of $8/8 \times 100 = 100$ IQ, which is the norm.

With adults this method of calculation does not apply. They would be judged on an 'IQ' test where the average score would be 100 and the results graded above and below this norm according to known test scores.

The distribution of IQ to the population takes the form of a fairly regular bell curve. On the Cattell scale of intelligence, for example, half the population would have an IQ of between 90 and 110 (half above 100 and half below), 25% scoring above 110 and 25% below 90. Above this central group about 14.5% of the population have IQs of 110–120; 7% have IQs of 120–130 and 3.5% IQs of 130 or above. Below the central group 14.5% have an IQ between 80 and 90, 7% between 70 and 80, and the remaining 3.5% below 70.

HOW IMPORTANT IS IT TO HAVE A HIGH IQ?

Cynics will say that the only thing having a high IQ proves is that the individual has scored well on an intelligence test. It does not follow that a person who is good at IQ tests is necessarily capable of excelling at academic tests, regardless of how logical and quick-witted he or she is. Motivation and dedication are sometimes more important than brain-power. There are many different types of intelligence which we can describe as genius, and people who have outstanding artistic, creative, sporting or practical prowess can all be highly successful without necessarily having a high-registered IQ. A good memory is yet another type of intelligence and could result in high academic success despite a low-measured IQ. Nevertheless, IQ tests have become commonplace in many institutions, and proficiency at IQ tests can significantly improve one's employment prospects.

Having a high IQ does not make you successful. All the other things you need to be a success – such as persistence, flair and imagination – do not necessarily follow. But it does give you a bit of self-confidence, and perhaps make you think you can achieve things if you put your mind to it.

WHAT IS AN INTELLIGENCE TEST?

Intelligence tests are a standardized examination devised to measure human intelligence as distinct from attainments. A test consists of a series of questions, exercises and/or tasks which have been set to many thousands of examinees.

WHAT TYPES OF QUESTION ARE INCLUDED IN INTELLIGENCE TESTS?

Vocabulary tests are widely used in intelligence testing. It is often said that to have a mastery of words is to have in one's possession the ability to produce order out of chaos. Numerical problems are often included in intelligence tests with the emphasis on number-association rather than on specific knowledge of formulae. There is also a swing now towards spatial tests using diagrams, with less emphasis on word knowledge. Advocates of this type of test argue that diagrammatic tests are culture-fair and test raw intelligence without the influence of prior knowledge.

WHAT ARE THE USES OF IQ TESTS?

In educational settings, intelligence tests are administered to assess the ability of individuals with the aim of improving instruction and curriculum-planning. Tests are commonplace in industrial and organizational settings for selection and classification. For many people, it is also important to know their own IQs to enable them to recognize and harness their own potential.

CAN I IMPROVE MY OWN IQ?

Mental age remains constant in development to about the age of thirteen, after which it is shown to slow up; and beyond the age of eighteen little or no improvement is found.

HOW, THEN, DO I SUCCEED AT IQ TESTS?

Although it is generally agreed that IQ is hereditary and remains fairly constant throughout life, it is possible to improve your performance on IQ tests by regular practice on the types of question that one may encounter in such tests.

A gymnast will improve his or her performance and increase his or her chances of success at whatever level at which he or she is competing by means of punishing training schedules and refinement of technique. In the same way, this book provides you with the mental gymnastics to give you the opportunity to increase your performance and succeed at IQ tests.

IQ tests are set and used on the assumption that those taking the test have no knowledge of the testing method itself and that they know very little about the question method itself within these tests. Therefore, it follows that if you learn something about this form of testing and know how to approach the different kinds of question you can improve your performance on the tests themselves. It is this improvement in performance that we have set out to achieve in the tests contained in this book. The fourteen tests have been specially compiled to include a wide variety of verbal, numerical and spatial content. As they have been specially compiled these tests are not standardized, so an actual IQ assessment is not given. They are intended as practice for anyone who may be asked to take an IQ test in the future, and a guide is given as a check of success in undertaking each of the fourteen separate tests and for taking all fourteen tests overall. Readers should note an improvement in their performance on successive tests undertaken as they become accustomed to the types of question encountered, and the type of thinking required to solve these questions.

HOW DO I USE THIS BOOK?

The book consists of fourteen separate tests for you to attempt each consisting of 30 questions. All tests are of approximately the same degree of difficulty. Each test has a rating. There is also an accumulative rating for all fourteen tests.

A time limit of 60 minutes is allowed for each test. The answers are given at the end of each test – award yourself one point for each correct answer. Some answers are provided with a detailed explanation, so that you can study in detail why you might have failed to find the correct answer.

Assessment:

ONE TEST		FOURTEEN TESTS	
SCORE	RATING	SCORE	RATING
27–30	Exceptional	378–420	Exceptional
24–26	Excellent	336–377	Excellent
20–23	Very good	280–335	Very good
15–19	Good	210–279	Good
10–14	Average	140–209	Average

BEFORE STARTING THE TESTS WOULD IT HELP TO SEE SOME EXAMPLES?

Yes. While there is no substitute for practising on actual tests, it is useful to have prior understanding of the types of question which may be encountered. The following are some examples of the types of question you will be asked to solve as you work through the fourteen tests.

Odd one out

We all have the ability to classify objects into groups. We all know, for example, that beech, elm, oak and willow are all trees, so that if we suddenly introduce daffodil into the list, it will then be the odd one out because it is a flower. This type of thinking is that which is required to solve the odd one out questions in this book; and also called for is flexibility of thought, in view of the different reasons why one item is the odd one out and because numerical and spatial questions can also be included in this category.

EXAMPLES

1. Which is the odd one out?

abode, dwelling, house, residence, street

Answer: street. The rest are specifically places in which we live. Street is a general term which may contain many houses, gardens, trees, pavements, road surfaces etc.

2. Which is the odd one out?

calm, quiet, relaxed, serene, unruffled

Answer: quiet. The rest all mean the same thing. However, your being quiet does not mean that you are calm, relaxed, serene and unruffled. You could be extremely upset and agitated but still remain quiet.

3. Which is the odd one out?

1, 3, 5, 9, 10

Answer: 10. This is an even number, whereas the rest are odd numbers.

4. Which is the odd one out?

7436, 5294, 9618, 3854, 9218

This is more difficult and an example of why flexibility of thought and a degree of lateral thinking is necessary. At first glance there doesn't seem to be an obvious reason why one of the numbers is different to the next. They are all even numbers, they each start with an odd digit. The second digit is always even, the third digit is always odd and all numbers have four different digits. So what can be the reason why one is different to the next? Well, try adding up the digits of each number and you will find that the total for each number is 20, except one of the numbers: 9618. Its digits 9 + 6 + 1 + 8 total 24, and this is therefore the odd one out.

5. Which is the odd one out?

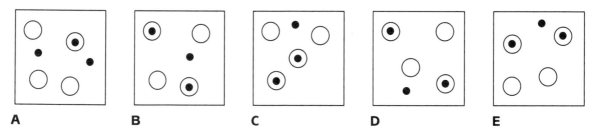

A   B   C   D   E

Answer: **A**. Each square contains three black dots and four circles. 'A' is the odd one out because only one circle contains a black dot. In all the other squares, two circles contain black dots.

6.   Which is the odd one out?

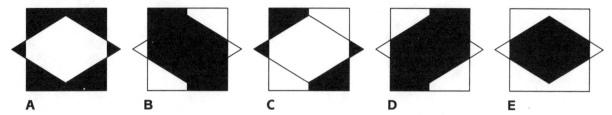

A   B   C   D   E

This again is much more difficult and lateral thinking is again necessary. All five figures consist of a diamond and a square with black and white shading. However, look at figures 'A' and 'E' and you will see the same pattern of shading but with black and white reversal. Further inspection will reveal the same analogy for figures 'C' and 'D'. This leaves figure 'B' on its own without a similar pairing and, therefore, the odd one out.

Synonyms and Antonyms

A *synonym* is a word having the *same meaning* as another of the same language.
An *antonym* is a word having the *opposite meaning* to another of the same language.
Both synonym tests and antonym tests are widely used in intelligence testing. Such tests can come in several different forms.

EXAMPLES

1.   Which word in the brackets means the same as the word in capital letters?

EASY (elementary, artful, infantile, pretentious, well)

Answer: elementary

2.   Which word in the brackets is opposite in meaning to the word in capital letters?

OBSCURE (deep, recondite, evident, answer, truth)

Answer: evident

3.   Which two words are closest in meaning?

solve, curious, inquire, advance, reason, probe

Answer: inquire, probe

4.   Which two words are opposite in meaning?

dark, true, slender, false, accuse, test

Answer: true, false

5.   Complete the words reading clockwise which are antonyms.

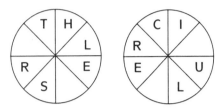

Answer: ruthless, merciful

Analogy

An analogy is a similitude of relations, where it is necessary to reason the answer from a parallel case. This type of question can also come in many different forms and can include verbal, numerical and spatial questions.

EXAMPLES

1.   HELMET is to protection as

TIARA is to (adornment, queen, hair, royalty, head).

Answer: adornment. Both a helmet and a tiara are worn on the head; however, a helmet is worn for protection and a tiara is worn for adornment.

2.   Choose the pair that best expresses a relationship similar to that of the pair in capitals.

ESTIMATE : SPECULATE

A   appraise : ruminate
B   assume : deem
C   devise : appraise
D   contemplate : meditate
E   deduce : mediate

Answer: **D.** contemplate : meditate. This is both an analogy and a synonym question. The words estimate and speculate are synonyms; therefore you are logically looking for two words listed that are also synonyms. The words contemplate and meditate meet this requirement and are, therefore, the correct answers.

3.   547 is to 475 as

328 is to (823, 382, 832, 283, 238)

Answer: 283. Although a number question, the answer is not mathematical. It is simply a matter of changing the sequence of numbers in the same way in both cases. In this example, the first figure is moved to become the last figure; so the second figure becomes the first figure and the last figure becomes the second figure.

4. 48 : 192 : 64

Which set of numbers below have the same relationship as the numbers above?

A 82 : 246 : 96
B 31 : 124 : 72
C 96 : 192 : 48
D 35 : 175 : 54
E 27 : 108 : 36

Answer: **E** 27 : 108 : 36. This time the reasoning does involve mathematics. Multiply the first number by 4 to obtain the second number, i.e. 48 × 4 = 192 and 27 × 4 = 108. Then divide the second number by 3 to arrive at the third number i.e. 192 ÷ 3 = 64 and 108 ÷ 3 = 36.

5.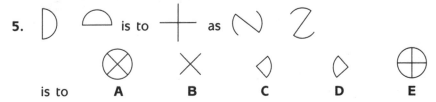

is to **A** **B** **C** **D** **E**

Answer: **B.** The first two figures are merged to form the final figure; however, in the final figure the curved lines disappear and only the straight lines remain.

Sequences
Sequences can include verbal questions but are mainly numerical or spatial.

EXAMPLE

1. 25, 23, 20, 16, **?** what number continues the sequence?

Answer: 11. Deduct 2, 3, 4, 5, in turn – i.e., the amount deducted increases by 1 each time

2.

which figure below continues the sequence?

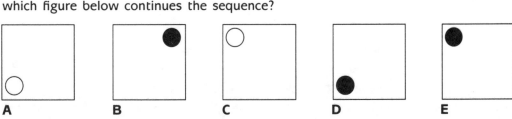

Answer: **E.** The dot moves round the square anti-clockwise visiting each corner of the square in turn, and is white then black in turn.

Matrix

As with sequences these can include verbal questions but are mainly numerical or spatial. Usually an array of nine squares is presented with the bottom right-hand square missing; this you have to find from a list of options. It is necessary to study the array as a whole or look across each horizontal line and down each vertical line to work out the logical pattern or progression that is occurring.

EXAMPLES

1. Which is the missing square?

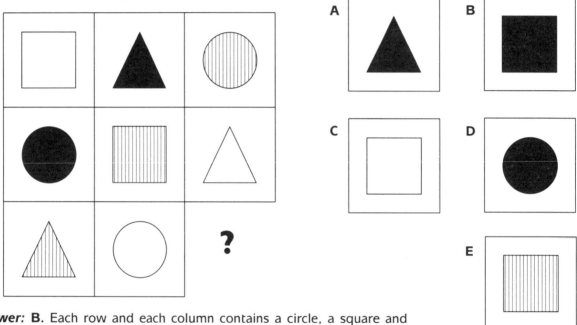

Answer: **B.** Each row and each column contains a circle, a square and a triangle. Also, each row and column contains a black, a white and a shaded figure.

2. What number should replace the question mark?

Answer: 17. Looking across each row the numbers increase by 2 each time. Looking down each column the numbers increase by 3 each time.

2	4	6	8
5	7	9	11
8	10	12	14
11	13	15	?

This set of examples is by no means a complete list, but is a selection of the types of question you may encounter and an example of the types of thought process you will need to apply. There will be many different variations of these examples, the occasional surprise item and several other types and unique type questions where it is also necessary to apply logical thought and lateral thinking.

TEST ONE

QUESTIONS

1. Which is the odd one out?

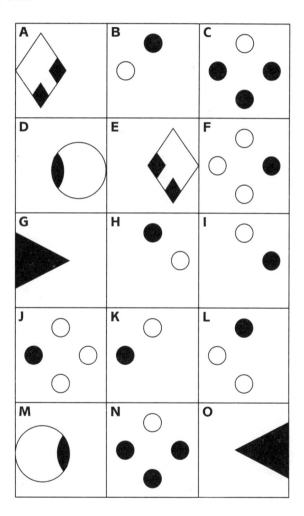

2. Which word in brackets is opposite in meaning to the word in capitals?

    KNACK (necessity, surplus, ineptitude, facility, quell)

3.

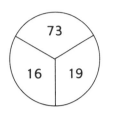 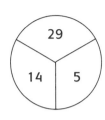 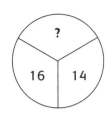

What number should replace the question mark?

A 54   **B** 56   **C** 58   **D** 60   **E** 62

4.   'moon panic' is an anagram of which 9-letter word?

5.   **A**   **B**   **C**   **D**   **E**   **F**   **G**   **H**

What letter is two to the left of the letter immediately to the right of the letter three to the left of the letter 'F'?

6.

What continues the above sequences?

A   **B**   **C**   **D**   **E**

7.   7653294 is to 3497526 as 6391854 is to:

> **A**   4156983
> **B**   1459638
> **C**   5146983
> **D**   1456893
> **E**   1456983

8.   Which one of these is not an anagram of a profession?

> **A**   WAR TIE
> **B**   OIL ART
> **C**   HOLD PIN
> **D**   RIOTED
> **E**   WRY ALE

9. Insert in the brackets a word that means the same as the definitions outside the brackets.

Pattern (. . . . .) fungus

10.

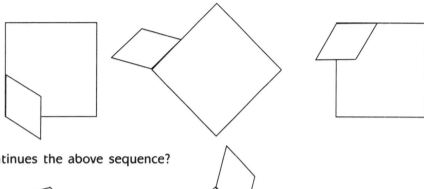

What continues the above sequence?

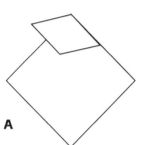

A

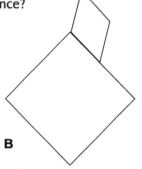

B

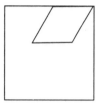

C

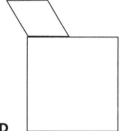

D

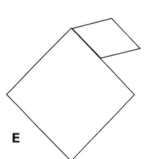

E

11. What is the value of: $\frac{2}{9} \div \frac{2}{7}$

A $\frac{4}{9}$ **B** $\frac{7}{15}$ **C** $\frac{7}{9}$ **D** $\frac{5}{7}$ **E** $\frac{8}{9}$

12. Complete the words reading clockwise. These words are synonyms.

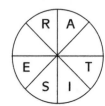

13. Which is the odd one out?

calypso, symphony, shanty, madrigal, aria

14. Out of 100 people surveyed, 84 had an egg for breakfast, 79 had bacon, 67 had toast and 87 coffee. How many people, at least, must have had all four items?

A 15   **B** 17   **C** 18   **D** 19   **E** 20

15. Which word in brackets is closest in meaning to the word in capitals?

ESCHEW (abscond, abandon, agree, advocate, amplify)

16. What is the name given to a group of MULES?

A HOVER
B ROOKERY
C CRY
D BARREN
E BUSINESS

17. Place in the brackets a word which means the same as the words outside the brackets

STAMP (. . . . .) OPEN

18. Which word when added to the first will make a new word and when placed in front of the second will also make a new word?

CABBAGE (. . . . .) WORK

19. Place 3 two-letter bits together to equal 'A form of money'.

UM   BA   WA   UR   MP   RT

20. SYMBOLS

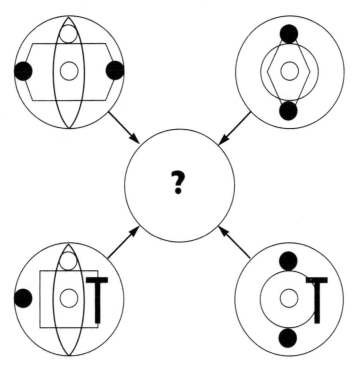

Each line and symbol which appears in the four outer circles above is transferred to the centre circle according to these rules:

If a line or symbol occurs in the outer circles

once:	it is transferred
twice:	it is possibly transferred
3 times:	it is transferred
4 times:	it is not transferred

Which of the circles A, B, C, D or E shown below should appear at the centre of the diagram above?

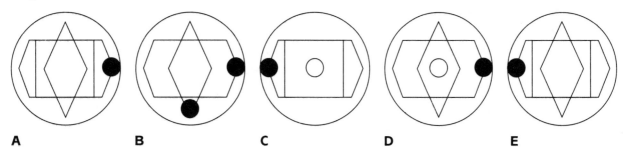

| A | B | C | D | E |

21. Which number should replace the **?**

17, 5, 14½, 8½, 12, 12, ?

22. Which number should replace the ?

(522)	9	52
(291)	16	21
(861)	?	24

23. Find the one-word anagram

A GRIM ERA

24. Find the two words which are SYNONYMS. Both words read clockwise.

25. COMPARISON

IF 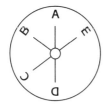 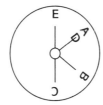 IS TO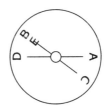

THEN 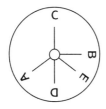 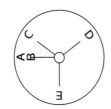 IS TO

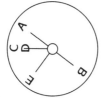 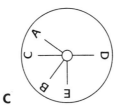 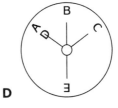 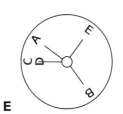

A   **B**   **C**   **D**   **E**

26. How many packets can be placed in the crate?

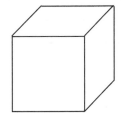 880mm × 460mm × 300mm

 220mm × 115mm × 75mm

27. Which number should replace the ?

28. Which number should replace the ?

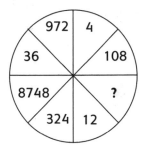

29. Find a word which when placed in front of these words make new words.

(. . . . . .)
STROKE
SINGER
SWITCH
PIECE
MIND

30. GRID

Each of the nine squares in the grid marked 1A to 3C, should incorporate all the lines and symbols which are shown in the squares of the same letter and number immediately above and to the left. For example, 2B should incorporate all the lines and symbols that are in 2 and B.

One of the squares is incorrect. Which one is it?

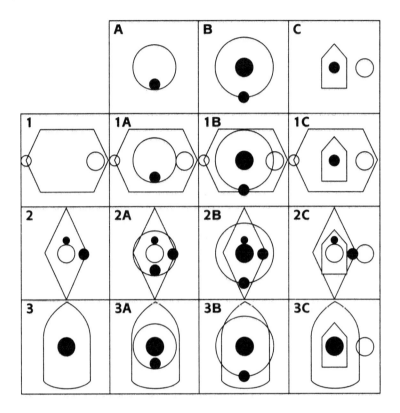

TEST ONE

ANSWERS

1. **L**   Every other square has an identical mirror image.
2. ineptitude
3. **C** 58 $73 - 16 \div 3 = 19$
$58 - 16 \div 3 = 14$
4. companion
5. **B**
6. **A**   The left half only of the first four figures are being repeated in the same sequence.
7. **E** 1456983   ABCDEFG   DGFACEB
6391854   1456983
8. **C**   HOLD PIN = Dolphin.
The professions are: waiter (WAR TIE), tailor (OIL ART), editor (RIOTED), lawyer (WRY ALE)
9. mould
10. **B**   The square is rotating through 45° at each stage and the diamond flips inside then outside the square at each stage.
11. **C** $\frac{1}{9}$ $\frac{2}{9} \div \frac{2}{7} = \frac{2}{9} \times \frac{7}{2} = \frac{14}{18} = \frac{7}{9}$
12. exercise, practise
13. symphony   This is purely music; the rest are songs.
14. **B**   17.   Add the percentages together, i.e. $84 + 79 + 67 + 87 = 317$. This gives 3 times each among 100 people and 4 to 17 people. The least percentage is, therefore 17.

15. abandon
16. **D**   BARREN
17. FRANK
18. PATCH
19. WAMPUM
20. **A**
21. $9\frac{1}{2}$ There are 2 series: 17, $14\frac{1}{2}$, 12, $9\frac{1}{2}$ ($-2\frac{1}{2}$); and 5, $8\frac{1}{2}$, 12, $15\frac{1}{2}$ ($+ 3\frac{1}{2}$).
22. 4   Reverse the order of digits in the outside numbers and divide the resultant right-hand number into the resultant left-hand number:
$861 \rightarrow 168$; $24 \rightarrow 42$; $168 \div 42 = 4$
23. MARRIAGE
24. MANIFEST, DISTINCT
25. **A**
26. 64
27. 23 $(6 \times 8) - 13 = 35$, $(7 \times 3) - 6 = 15$, $(9 \times 5) - 22 = 23$
28. 2916   The number start at the lowest, 4, and each third number in a clockwise direction, is obtained by multiplying by 3, i.e: 4 – 12 – 36 – 108 – 324 – 972 – 2916 – 8748.
29. MASTER
30. 2C

TEST TWO

1.

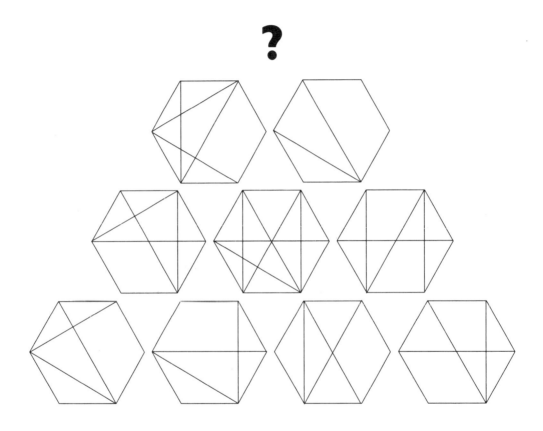

Which hexagon is missing from the top of the pyramid?

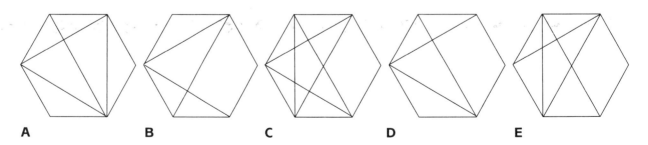

A   B   C   D   E

2. UNCANNY : EERIE
Choose the pair that best expresses a relationship similar to that of the pair above.

        A whimsical : esoteric
        B stubborn : erratic
        C outlandish : bizarre
        D fanciful : deviant
        E weird   : droll

3. What number should replace the **?**

    A 3   **B** 4   **C** 5   **D** 6   **E** 7

3	2	2	4
1	6	4	4
2	4	5	2
3	5	2	?

4. 'index pete' is an anagram of which 9-letter word?

5. Which is the missing tile?

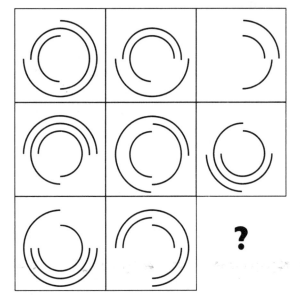

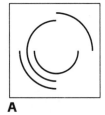
    A

    B

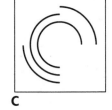
    C

    D

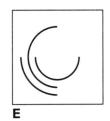
    E

6.   Which one of these is not an anagram of a type of dance?

> **A**   TIN EMU
> **B**   USA MAST
> **C**   ROB LEO
> **D**   VET GOAT
> **E**   IN HOPPER

7.   At each stage the dot moves one segment anticlockwise and the circle moves two segments anticlockwise. After how many stages do the two first appear in the same segment?

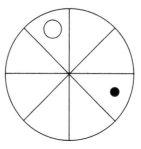

8.   Insert in the brackets a word that means the same as the definitions outside the brackets?

close and friendly (. . . . .) drop a hint

9.   Which is the odd one out?

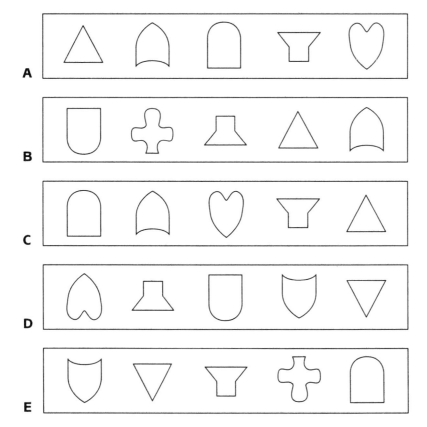

10. Complete the words reading clockwise. The words are synonyms.

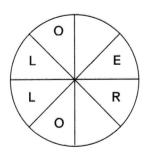 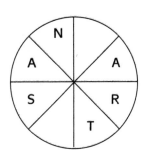

11. 7599 : 2835 : 240

Which group of numbers below have the same relationship as that of the numbers above?

     A 3599 : 1643 : 110
     B 6849 : 1949 : 313
     C 9474 : 3129 : 480
     D 8478 : 1792 : 126
     E 7632 : 1841 : 690

12. Which is the odd one out?

     chair, sofa, cabinet, bench, pew

13.

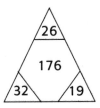 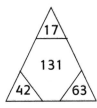 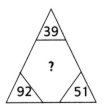

Which number should replace the question mark?

A 117   **B** 127   **C** 137   **D** 147   **E** 157

14. Underline the two words that are closest in meaning.

     complex, logical, garrulous, exact, rational, scientific

15. Underline the two words that are opposite in meaning.

     apathetic, laconic, tearful, heavy, verbose, lifeless

16. Which number should replace the ?

     4, −11, 30.25, ?

17. Put in the brackets a word which means the same as the words outside the brackets.

PROTECT (. . . .) TOWER

18. Place 3 two-letter bits together to equal a 'High Official'.

CZ   ZI   AT   ER   IL   VI

19. What is the name given to a group of CURS?

> **A**   BROOD
> **B**   COWARDICE
> **C**   KINDLE
> **D**   ERST
> **E**   MELODY

20. COMPARISON

   IS TO

AS

   IS TO

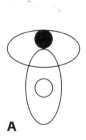            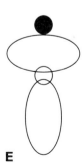

A   **B**   **C**   **D**   **E**

21. Which number should replace the **?**

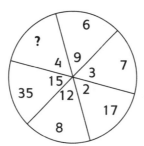

22. Which number should replace the **?**

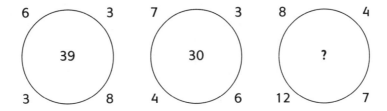

23. Which word when added to the first will make a new word and when placed in front of the second will also make a new word?

DOUBLE (. . . . .) WORD

24. Find the one-word anagram
VOICES RANT ON

25. HEXAGONS

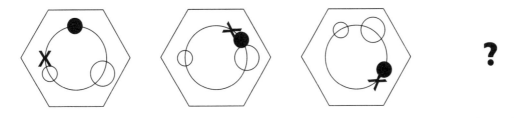

Which hexagon below continues the sequence?

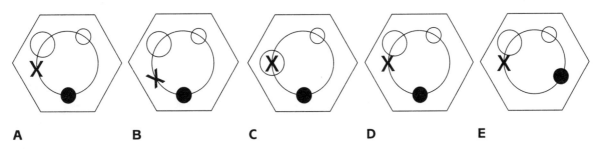

A   B   C   D   E

26. Which number should replace the **?**

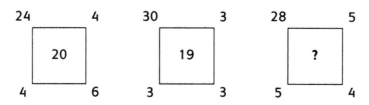

27. Which number should replace the **?**

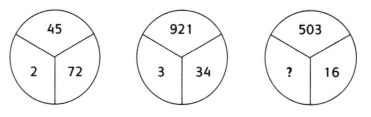

28. Find the two words which are **SYNONYMS**. Both words read clockwise.

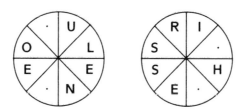

29. Find a 6-letter word made up of these 4 letters only.

FE
CN

30. SYMBOLS

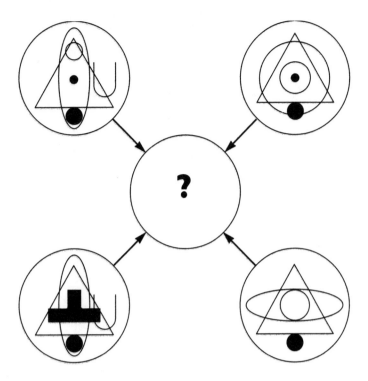

Each line and symbol which appears among the four outer circles above is transferred to the centre circle according to these rules:

If a line or symbol occurs in the outer circles

        once: it is transferred

        twice: it is possibly transferred

        3 times: it is transferred

        4 times: it is not transferred

Which of the circles A, B, C, D, or E shown below, should appear at the centre of the diagram above?

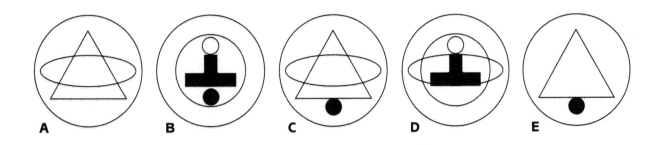

TEST TWO

ANSWERS

1. **E** Each hexagon has its contents determined by the contents of the two hexagons immediately below it. Where two lines appear in the same position in these two hexagons they are not carried forward to the hexagon immediately above it. Lines that appear just once are carried forward.

2. **C** outlandish : bizarre

3. **E** 7 Looking both across and down, the sum of each pair of numbers is one more than that of the previous pair of numbers.

4. expedient

5. **A** Looking across and down, any lines common to the first two tiles are not carried forward to the third tile.

6. **B** USA MAST = satsuma. The dances are: minuet (TIN EMU), bolero (ROB LEO), gavotte (VET GOAT) and hornpipe (IN HOPPER)

7. 5

8. intimate

9. **C** 'A' contains the same symbols as 'D' upside down and reversed. Similarly 'B' contains the same as 'E'.

10. follower, partisan

11. **D** 8478 : 1792 : 126
$8 \times 4 \times 7 \times 8 = 1792$,
$1 \times 7 \times 9 \times 2 = 126$

12. cabinet All the others are for sitting on.

13. **C** 137 reverse corner numbers and add, i.e. $93 + 29 + 15 = 137$.

14. logical, rational

15. laconic, verbose

16. –83.1875 Multiply each successive figure by $-2\frac{3}{4}$ (–2.75).

17. KEEP

18. VIZIER

19. **B** COWARDICE

20. **B**

21. 34 $(6 \times 12) = (8 \times 9)$; $(7 \times 15) = (3 \times 35)$; $(17 \times 4) = (2 \times 34)$

22. 8 $(6 \times 8) - (3 \times 3) = 39$; $(7 \times 6) - (3 \times 4) = 30$; $(8 \times 7) - (4 \times 12) = 8$

23. CROSS

24. CONVERSATION/CONSERVATION

25. **A**

26. 32: $(24 \div 6) + (4 \times 4) = 20$; $(30 \div 3) + (3 \times 3) = 19$; $(28 \div 4) + (5 \times 5) = 32$.

27. 5: Reverse numbers and divide: $54 \div 27 = 2$; $129 \div 43 = 3 =$; $305 \div 61 = 5$.

28. OPULENCE, RICHNESS

29. FENNEC

30. **D**

TEST THREE

QUESTIONS

1. Complete the words reading clockwise. The words are synonyms.

2.

? What comes next?

A 4 / 9 / 3   B 6 / 9 / 4   C 4 / 3 / 6   D 4 / 9 / 6   E 6 / 9 / 3

3.

?

What comes next?

A

B

C

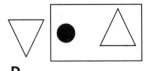

D

E

4. 'been Allan' is an anagram of which girl's name?

5. 0, 0, 1, 3, 3, 4, 6, ?

What comes next in this sequence?

6. What creature name is missing from the brackets reading downwards to complete the three-letter words?

CU (_)
ER (_)
BE (_)
DO (_)
CU (_)
FU (_)

7. Insert in the brackets a word that means the same as the definitions outside the brackets.
in good condition (. . .) a sudden spell of emotion

8.

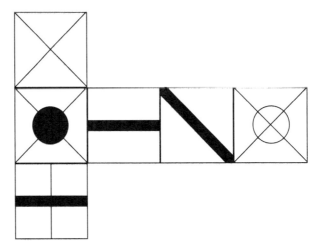

When the above is folded to form a cube, just one of the following can be produced. Which one?

A   **B**   **C**   **D**   **E**

9. Which two words are closest in meaning?

plebiscite, résumé, referendum, recommendation, decision, system

10. A train travelling at a speed of 75 mph enters a tunnel that is 2 miles long. The length of the train is ½ mile. How long does it take for all of the train to pass through the tunnel from the moment the front enters to the moment the rear emerges?

A   2 mins   **B**   2 mins 5 secs   **C**   2 mins 10 secs
D   2 mins 15 secs   **E**   2 mins 20 secs

11. Which two words are opposite in meaning?

keen, hopeful, singular, redolent, sorry, reluctant

12.

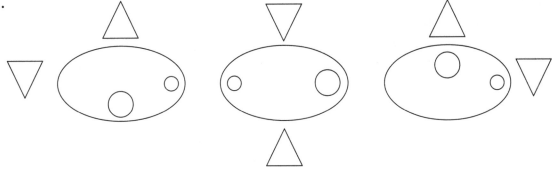

What continues the above sequence?

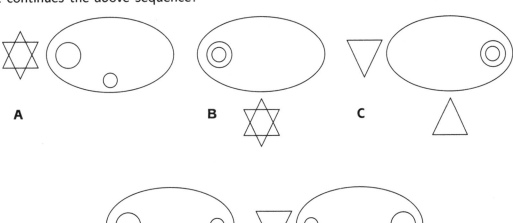

A   **B**   **C**

D   **E**

13. Which one of these is not an anagram of a type of drink?

A	RAM IT IN
B	COLD AIR
C	RICH DO
D	BY DARN
E	AND SHY

14. 5947, 5238, 1484, ?

Which comes next?

A 369   **B** 792   **C** 844   **D** 968   **E** 1042

15. To which square on the right can a dot be added so that it meets the same conditions as the box on the left?

A   **B**   **C**   **D**   **E**

16. Which number should replace the ?

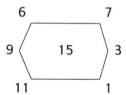   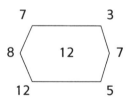   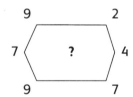

17. Find the one-word anagram.

NO MORE STARS

18. Put in the brackets a word which means the same as the words outside the brackets

ISLAND (. . . . . .) JUMPER

19. Which word, when placed on the end of the first word will make a new word, and when placed in front of the second word will also make a new word?

SUMMER (. . . .) PIECE

20. Which is the odd one out?

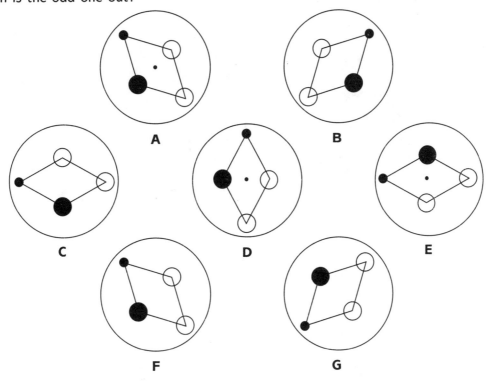

21. Which number should replace the ?

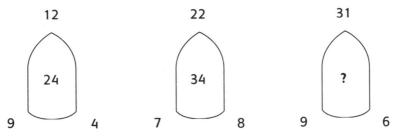

22. Place 3 two-letter bits together to equal 'a breakfast food'.

LI   CO   MU   KE   ES   RF

23. What is the name given to a group of LAPWING?

        A   STATE
        B   SUBTILTE
        C   DECEIT
        D   FLIGHT
        E   HUSK

24. Find a 6-letter word which is made up of these 4 letters only.

XE
AN

25. SYMBOLS

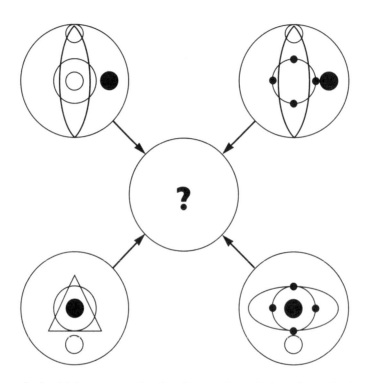

Each line and symbol which appears in the four outer circles above is transferred to the centre circle according to these rules:

If a line or symbol occurs in the outer circles

once:	it is transferred
twice:	it is possibly transferred
3 times:	it is transferred
4 times:	it is not transferred

Which of the circles A, B, C, D or E shown below should appear at the centre of the diagram above?

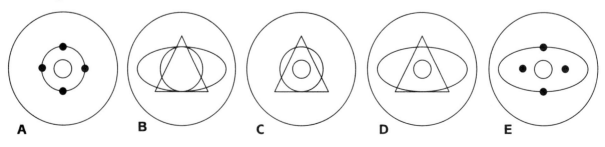

A　　　　B　　　　C　　　　D　　　　E

26. Find a word which when placed in front of each of these words makes new words.

(. . .)

. HEAD
. MONEY
. STRIPE
. PRICK
. HOLE

27. Which number replaces the ?

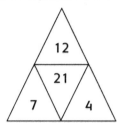 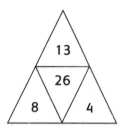 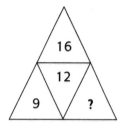

28. Fill in the two words which are SYNONYMS. Both words read clockwise.

29. Which number should replace the ?

28, 30, 32, 33, 34, 35, 36, ?

30. Which circle will continue the sequence?

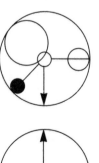 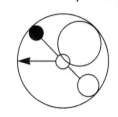 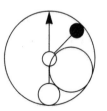

 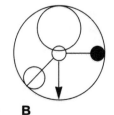 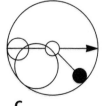 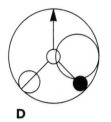 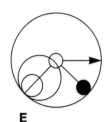

A   **B**   **C**   **D**   **E**

TEST THREE

ANSWERS

1. indicate, register.

2. **D**

4
9
6

Reverse column and drop the lowest number each time.

3. **D** The dot moves from side to side of the rectangle at each stage. The upward pointing triangle also moves from side to side of the rectangle at each stage. The downward pointing triangle moves from right to left one position at each stage.

4. Annabelle

5. **6** The sequence runs +0, +1, +2 and then is repeated.

6. BADGER, from cuB, erA, beD, doG, cuE, fuR

7. fit

8. **D**

9. plebiscite, referendum

10. **A** 2 mins The actual distance travelled by the rear of the train was 2½ miles – the first half-mile being outside the entrance of the tunnel while the front was already inside, and the remaining 2 miles as the rear passed completely through. At 75 mph, it takes 1 hour = 60 minutes to travel 75 miles, or 5 miles in 4 minutes. So 2½ miles (= ½ × 5 miles) takes ½ × 4 minutes = 2 minutes.

11. keen, reluctant

12. **B** The small circle moves backwards and forwards in the ellipse. The large circle is moving round each side of the ellipse at each stage anticlockwise. The upward triangle moves up and down outside the ellipse. The downward triangle moves round the outside of the ellipse clockwise.

13. **C** RICH DO = orchid. The drinks are: martini (RAM IT IN), cordial (COLD AIR), brandy (BY DARN), shandy (AND SHY).

14. **B** 792   1484   18 × 44 = 792

15. **C** So that the dot is in both triangle and large circle.

16. 12 (6 + 9 + 11) – (7 + 3 + 1) = 15; (7 + 8 + 12) – (3 + 7 + 5) = 12; (9 + 7 + 9) – (2 + 4 + 7) = 12

17. ASTRONOMERS

18. JERSEY

19. TIME

20. **B**

21. 23 (9 × 4) – 12 = 24; (7 × 8) – 22 = 34; (9 × 6) – 31 = 23.

22. MUESLI

23. DECEIT

24. ANNEXE

25. **D**

26. PIN

27. 12 (7 × 12) ÷ 21 = 4; (13 × 8) ÷ 26 = 4; (16 × 9) ÷ 12 = 12.

28. BLOCKADE, ENCIRCLE

29. 38   All non-prime numbers.

30. **E**

TEST FOUR

QUESTIONS

1. Which three of these pieces can be fitted together to form a cube?

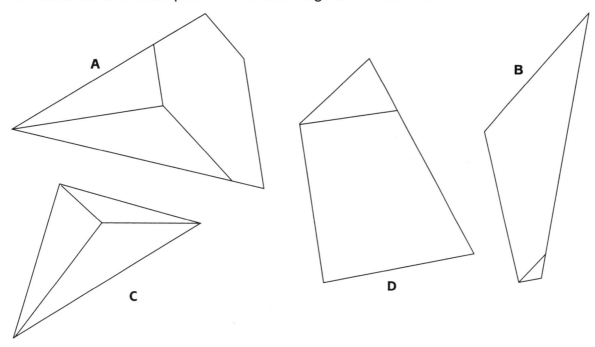

2. 76 (2) 37
   68 (4) 43
   97 (?) 33

   What number is missing from the bracket?

   A 5   **B** 6   **C** 7   **D** 8   **E** 9

3. OASIS : SAND

   Choose the pair that best expresses a relationship similar to that of the pair above.

   A desert   : trees
   B forest   : trees
   C island   : water
   D everglades : swamp
   E channel   : water

4. Which word in brackets is opposite in meaning to the word in capitals?

ORDINARY (unknown, long, historic, prudent, affluent)

5. ROOT A PINE is an anagram of which 9-letter word?

6.

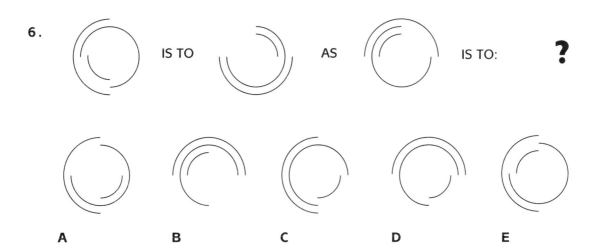

A   B   C   D   E

7. Complete the words reading clockwise. The words are antonyms.

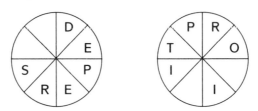

8. What us the missing number?

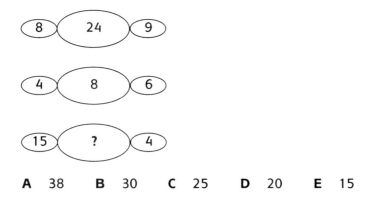

A 38   **B** 30   **C** 25   **D** 20   **E** 15

9. Which is the odd one out?

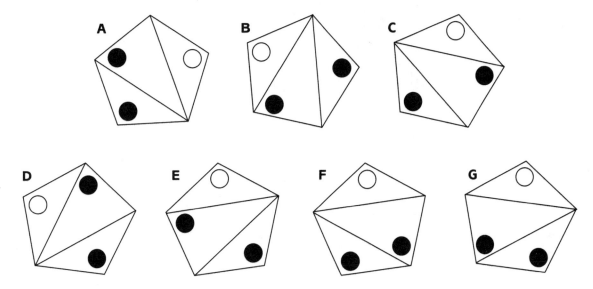

10. Which one of these is not an anagram of a type of food?

A IT IS CUB
B AM LISA
C PEAK CAN
D CLAIRE
E MICRONS

11. How many minutes before 9 a.m. is it if one hour later it will be three times as many minutes past 9 a.m.?

12. Insert in the brackets a word that means the same as the definitions outside the brackets.

sleeveless garment (. . . .) a promontory

13. Which is the odd one out?

dispute, fracas, altercation, annoyance, squabble

14. Which word in brackets means the same as the word in capitals?

HAUGHTY (willing, conceited, august, unhelpful, subservient)

15.

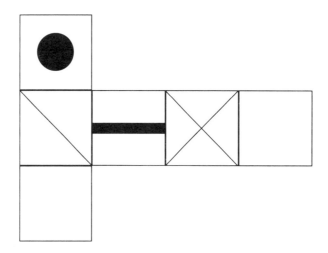

When the above is folded to form a cube, just one of the following can be produced. Which one?

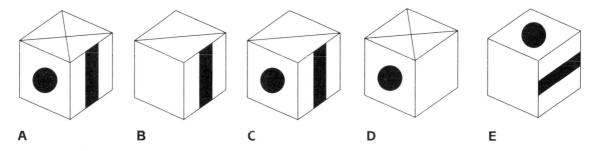

A   B   C   D   E

16. Which number should replace the **?**

-4, 9, -2½, 6¼, -1, 3½, **?**

17. Place 3 two-letter bits together to equal 'GIVE ADVICE'.

BI   PU   KI   RW   TZ   CE

18. Place a word after the first word to make a new two-word expression, and place that same extra word in front of the second word to make another two-word expression.

CLOCK (. . . . .) BRIDGE

19. Put in the brackets a word which means the same as the words outside the brackets.

BODY (. . . .) CELEBRATION

20. SYMBOLS

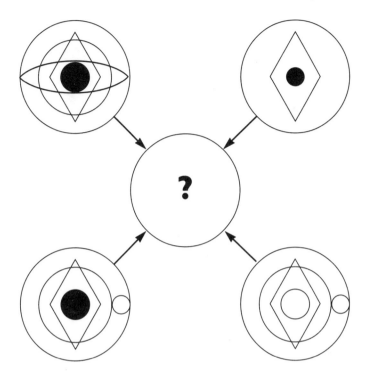

Each line and symbol which appears in the four outer circles above is transferred to the centre circle according to these rules:

If a line or symbol occurs in the outer circles

once:	it is transferred
twice:	it is possibly transferred
3 times:	it is transferred
4 times:	it is not transferred

Which of the circles A, B, C, D or E shown below should appear at the centre of the diagram above?

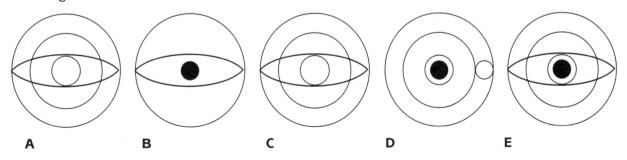

A   B   C   D   E

21. Which number should replace the **?**

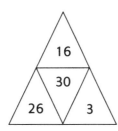 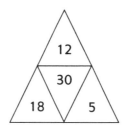 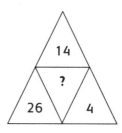

22. What is the name given to a group of GOATS?

     A FLOCK
     B GRIST
     C GRAND
     D HERD
     E HAND

23. HEXAGONS
Which hexagon below continues the sequence?

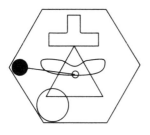 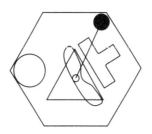 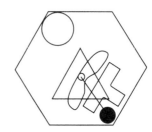 **?**

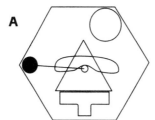 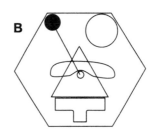

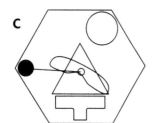 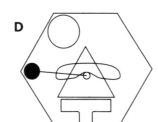 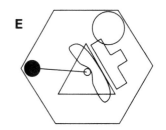

24. Find the two words which are SYNONYMS. Both words read clockwise.

25. Find a 6-letter word which is made up of these 4 letters only.

KL
ET

26. Insert a word that completes the first word and starts the second word.

WORKMAN (. . . .) WRIGHT

27. Which number should replace the **?**

  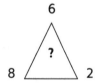

28. Find the one-word anagram.

EVIL FAST

29. Which number should replace the **?**

14, 19, 29, 40, 44, 52, ?

30. GRID

Each of the nine squares in the grid marked 1A to 3C, should incorporate all the lines and symbols which are shown in the squares of the same letter and number immediately above and to the left. For example, 2B should incorporate all the lines and symbols that are in 2 and B.

One of the squares is incorrect. Which one is it?

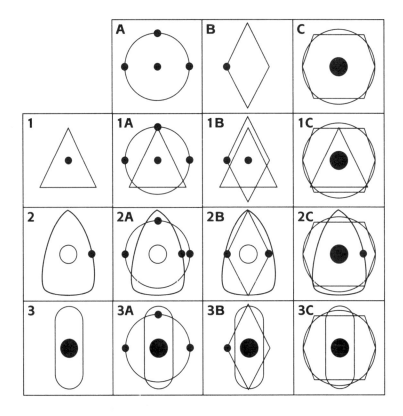

TEST FOUR

ANSWERS

1.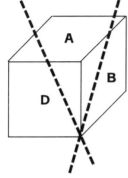

2. **C** 7 $9 \times 7 = 63$ $3 \times 3 = 9$
   $63 \div 9 = 7$

3. **C**:   island : water. An oasis is surrounded by sand, and an island is surrounded by water.

4. historic

5. operation

6. **C**   The large arc moves 90° anti-clockwise.
   The middle arc moves 90° clockwise.
   The inner arc moves 180°.

7. persuade, prohibit

8. **D** 20 $15 \times 4 = 60$ $60 \div 3 = 20$

9. **F**   All the others have an identical pairing.

10. **E**   MICRONS = crimson. The foods are: biscuit (IT IS CUB), salami (AM LISA), pancake (PEAK CAN), eclair (CLAIRE).

11. 15 minutes

12. cape

13. annoyance All the others are synonyms.

14. conceited

15. **A**

16. ½ There are 2 series −4, −2½, −1, ½ (+ 1½); and 9, 6¼, 3½, ¾, (−2¾).

17. KIBITZ

18. TOWER

19. MASS

20. **E**

21. 48 $(26 − 16) \times 3 = 30$; $(18 − 12) \times 5 = 30$; $(26 − 14) \times 4 = 48$.

22. **D**   HERD

23. **A**

24. LIBERATE, UNFASTEN

25. KETTLE

26. SHIP

27. 28 $(7 + 2) \times 4 = 36$; $(8 + 5) \times 5 = 65$; $(6 + 8) \times 2 = 28$.

28. FESTIVAL

29. 59   Add digits to previous numbers.
    $14 + 1 + 4 = 19 + 1 + 9 = 29 + 2 + 9 = 40 + 4 + 0 = 44 + 4 + 4 = 52 + 5 + 2 = 59$

30. 2A

TEST FIVE

QUESTIONS

1.

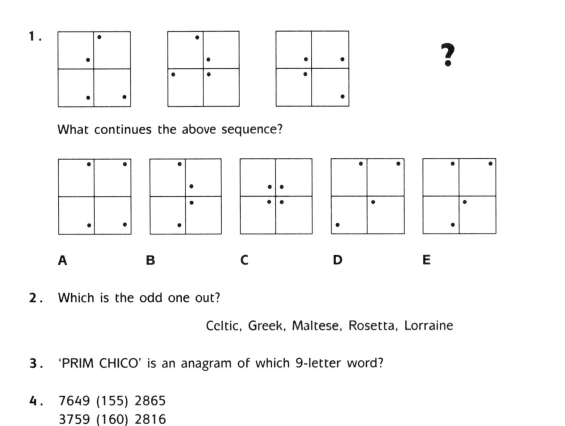

What continues the above sequence?

A   B   C   D   E

2. Which is the odd one out?

Celtic, Greek, Maltese, Rosetta, Lorraine

3. 'PRIM CHICO' is an anagram of which 9-letter word?

4. 7649 (155) 2865
   3759 (160) 2816
   4299 (?) 7412

   What number is missing?

   A 70   **B** 80   **C** 90   **D** 110   **E** 120

5. **A**   **B**   **C**   **D**   **E**   **F**   **G**   **H**

   What letter is immediately to the left of the letter three to the right of the letter immediately to the right of the letter 'B'?

6. The houses are numbers 1, 2, 3, 4, etc. up one side of the street, then back down the other side. Opposite number 29 is number 52. How many houses in the street?

7.

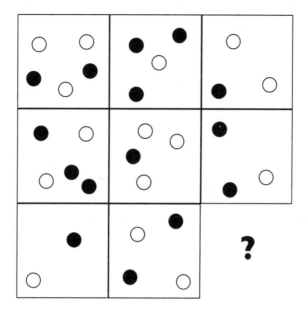

Which is the missing tile?

A   B   C   D   E

8. Complete the words reading clockwise. The words are antonyms.

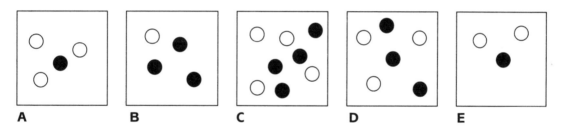

9. Which is the odd one out?

acquit, condone, exonerate, absolve, vindicate

10. What number continues the sequence?

25, 50, 27, 46, 31, 38, 39, **?**

11. Which one of these is not an anagram of a type of card game?

> **A** RIG BED
> **B** HER CUE
> **C** ON NO TOP
> **D** REP OK
> **E** BEG A CAB

12. Which two words are opposite in meaning?

> destroy, mislay, seek, find, obtain, acquire

13. Insert in the brackets a word that means the same as the definitions outside the brackets.

> encircle (. . . .) resonate

14.

9	26	17	9
32	57	?	32
23	31	8	23
9	26	17	9

What number should replace the question mark?

A 22   **B** 23   **C** 24   **D** 25   **E** 26

15. Which two words are closest in meaning?

> docile, supple, resilient, settled, talented, useful

16. Which number should replace the **?**

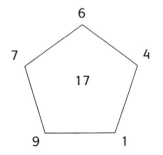 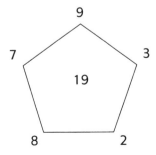 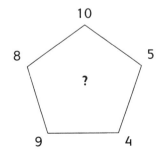

17. Put in the brackets a word which means the same as the words outside the brackets.

HINGED SEAT (. . . . .) DAGGER

18. Find the one-word anagram.

EVIL'S AGENTS

19. Place a word behind the first word to make a new word with the first word, and in front of the second word to make a new word with the second word.

CROSS (. . . .) RAGE

20. CIRCLES
Which of A, B, C, D or E, fits into the blank circle to carry on a logical sequence?

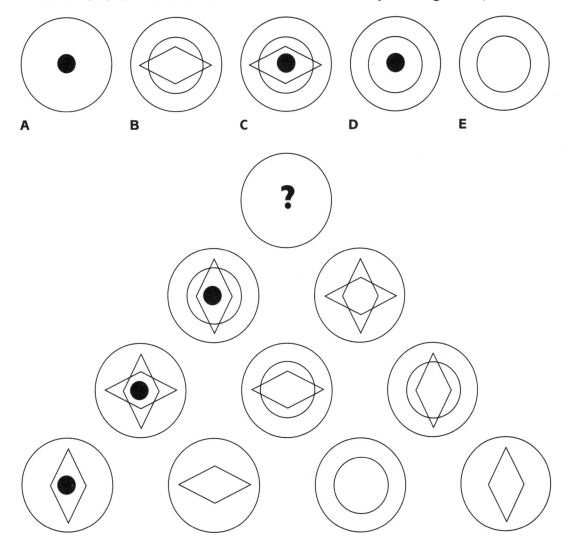

21. Which number should replace the **?**

8	28	7	28
9	12	4	24
7	37	9	26
12	13	2	?

22. What is the name given to a group of HERRINGS?

      A   BATCH
      B   CLUTCH
      C   FESNYNG
      D   GLEAN
      E   CLUSTER

23. Find a 6-letter word which is made up of these 4 letters only.

MR
EU

24. Which number should replace the **?**

8, –14, ?, –42.875

25. COMPARISON

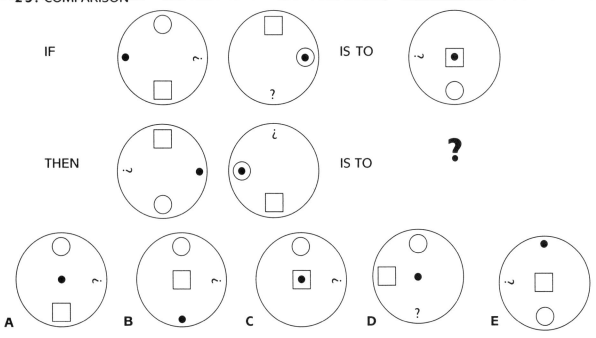

26. Which is the odd one out?

plait, embroil, twist, braid, interlace

27. Place 3 two-letter bits together to equal 'A robe'.

NO   LO   KI   PI   MO   SA

28.

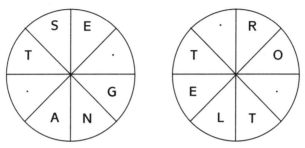

Find the two words which are synonyms. One read reads clockwise, the other anti-clockwise.

29. Find a word which when placed in front of each of these words makes new words.

(. . .)

. BURN
. BLIND
. DECK
. DOWN
. BEAM

30. Which is the odd one out?

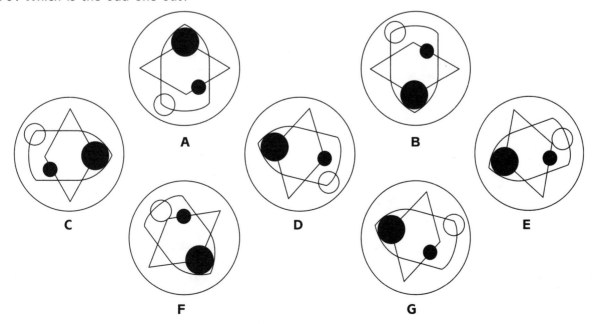

A   B   C   D   E   F   G

TEST FIVE
ANSWERS

1. **E** The dot in the top left-hand quarters moves up and down in two corners. The dot in the bottom left-hand quarter moves clockwise one corner at a time. The dot in the top right-hand quarter moves anticlockwise one corner at a time. The dot in the bottom right-hand quarter moves backwards and forwards between two corners.

2. Rosetta, this is a famous stone; the rest are crosses.

3. microchip

4. **A** 70   4299, 7412   29 + 41 = 70

5. **E**

6. 80

7. **D** So that there are six black and six white dots in each horizontal and vertical line.
   Alternatively you may have correctly reasoned that each row and each column has a combination of 1, 2 and 3 black dots as well as a combination of 1, 2 and 3 white dots. This leads to the same answer, tile D, which has 3 black and 3 white dots to complete these sequences in both the 3rd column and the 3rd row.

8. sluggish, animated

9. condone The rest are synonyms.

10. 22   There are two separate sequences. The first, starting with 25 jumps to alternate numbers adding 2, 4, 8 etc. The second, starting with 50 jumps to alternate numbers subtracting 4, 8, 16 etc.

11. **E** BEG A CAB = Cabbage. The card games are: bridge (RIG BED), euchre (HER CUE), pontoon (ON NO TOP), poker (REP OK).

12. mislay, find

13. ring

14. **D** 25   Looking across and down, the third and fourth numbers are the difference between the two previous numbers.

15. supple, resilient

16. 18   (9 + 7 + 6) – (4 + 1) = 17
    (9 + 7 + 8) – (3 + 2) = 19
    (10 + 8 + 9) – (5 + 4) = 18

17. MISERICORD

18. EVANGELISTS

19. ROAD

20. **C**

21. 11   (8 × 7) – 28 = 28; (9 × 4) – 12 = 24; (7 × 9) – 37 = 26;
    (12 × 2) – 13 = 11.

22. **D** GLEAN

23. MUMMER

24. 24.5 each number multiplied by –1.75 or 24½ each number multiplied by –1¾

25. **C**

26. embroil

27. KIMONO

28. STRANGLE, THROTTLE

29. SUN

30. **D**

TEST SIX

QUESTIONS

1.

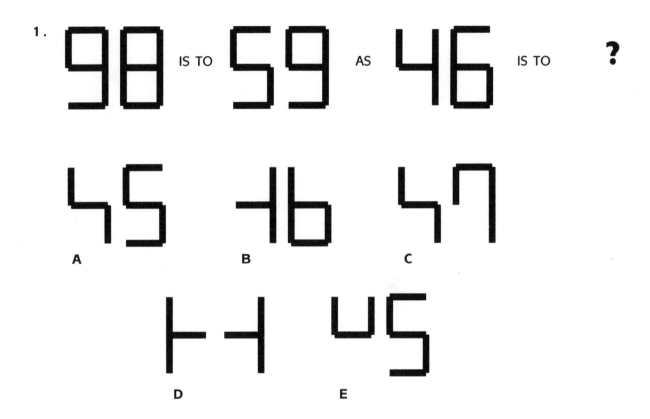

2. Complete the words reading clockwise. The words are antonyms.

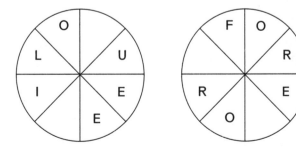

3. 5723 : 1311 : 143

Which group of numbers below has the same relationship as that of the numbers above?

     A   7649 : 3724 : 888
     B   5935 : 1422 : 103
     C   6279 : 3418 : 222
     D   7654 : 3892 : 792
     E   1581 : 129   : 33

4. Which is the odd one out?

succinct, terse, witty, pithy, concise

5.

What continues the sequence?

A   **B**   **C**   **D**   **E**

6.

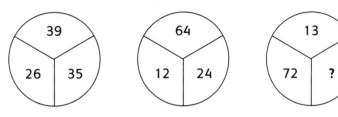

What number should replace the question mark?

A 15   **B** 16   **C** 17   **D** 18   **E** 19

7. What creature name is missing from the brackets, reading downwards to complete the three-letter words?

EL (_)
BE (_)
HE (_)
FA (_)
AC (_)
DO (_)

8. 'ARAB CHILD' is an anagram of which boy's name?

9. Which word in brackets means the same as the word in capitals?

SUMPTUOUS (extensive, frugal, opulent, exquisite, sufficient)

10. What number should replace * in the fourth column?

9	4	3	7	4	2
8	2	8	2	8	7
3	8	4	*	1	1
5	9	6	9	4	5

11. Which one of these is not an anagram of a type of sport?

A   OK SENOR
B   NIL GANG
C   CASH PIN
D   A TAKER
E   IN NETS

12. Which two words are opposite in meaning?

entice, tarry, confuse, tame, rush gossip

13.

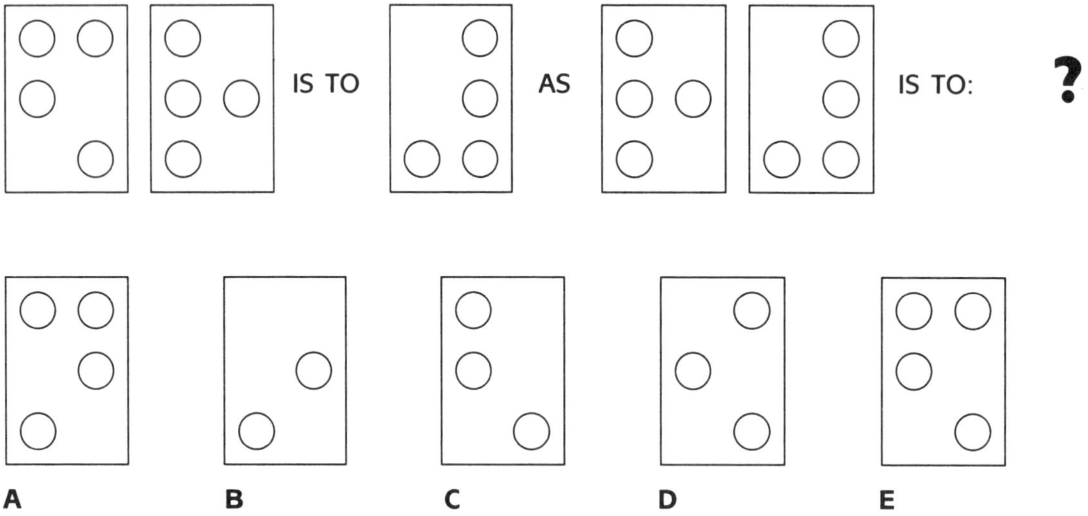
IS TO
AS
IS TO:
?
A
B
C
D
E

14.

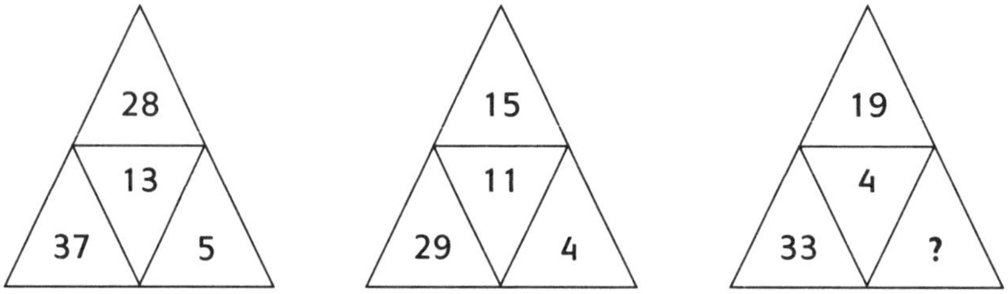
28
13
37
5
15
11
29
4
19
4
33
?

What number should replace the question mark?

A 11 **B** 12 **C** 13 **D** 14 **E** 15

15. Insert in the brackets a word that means the same as the definitions outside the brackets.

leave high and dry (. . . . . .) dark colour

16. Which number should replace the **?**

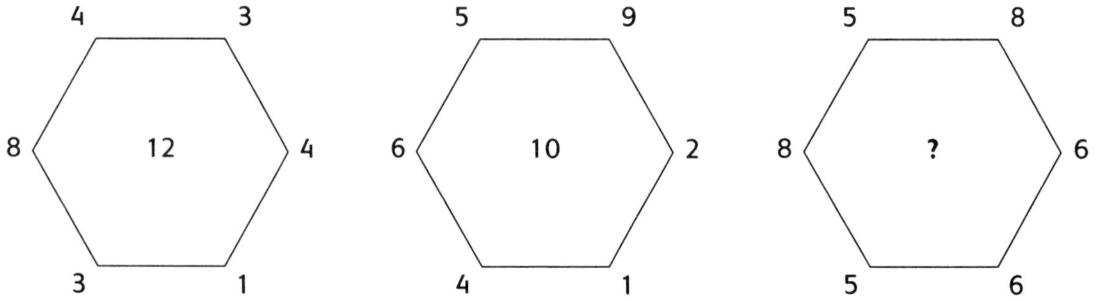
4
3
8
12
4
3
1
5
9
6
10
2
4
1
5
8
8
?
6
5
6

17. Find a word which when placed on the end of the first makes a new word, and when placed on the front of the second word makes a new word.

DOUBLE (. . . . .) PATCH

18. Put in the brackets a word which means the same as the words outside the brackets.

ABLE TO MOVE (. . . . . .) HANGING STRUCTURE

19. Find a 6-letter word which is made up of these 4 letters only.

LO
NG

20.

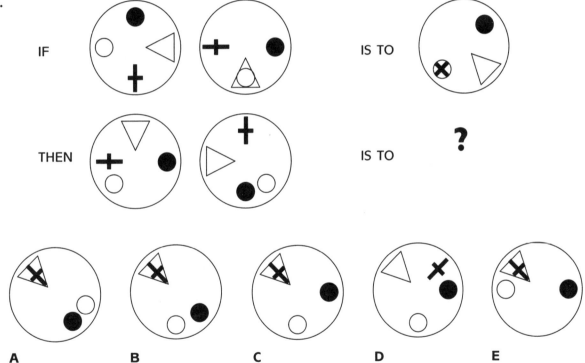

IF ... THEN ... IS TO ... IS TO ?

A   B   C   D   E

21. Insert a word which means the same as the two words outside the brackets.

HASTEN (. . . .) BREED

22. Place 3 two-letter bits together to equal FERTILE.

ND   SI   FE   CU   PA   LO

23. What is the name given to the group of CURLEW?

        A HEAD
        B HARASS
        C HILL
        D SWARM
        E FLIGHT

24. Find the one-word anagram.

IS NO AMITY

25. Which of these is the odd one out?

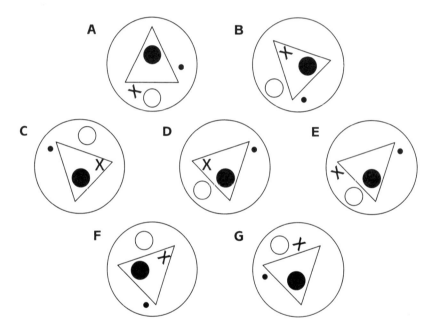

26. Which two words are opposite in meaning?

livid, confused, sporadic, impossible, delighted, remorseless

27. Which number should replace the **?**

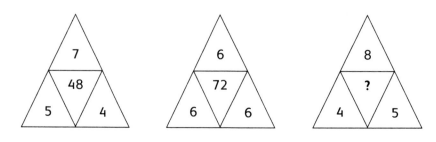

28. Find the two words which are synonyms. Both words read clockwise.

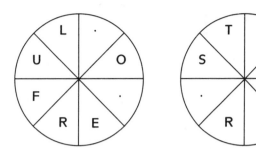

29. Underline the two words which are closet in meaning.

infernal, sagacious, replicate, wonder, demonic, effusive

30. HEXAGON

Which hexagon fits the missing space?

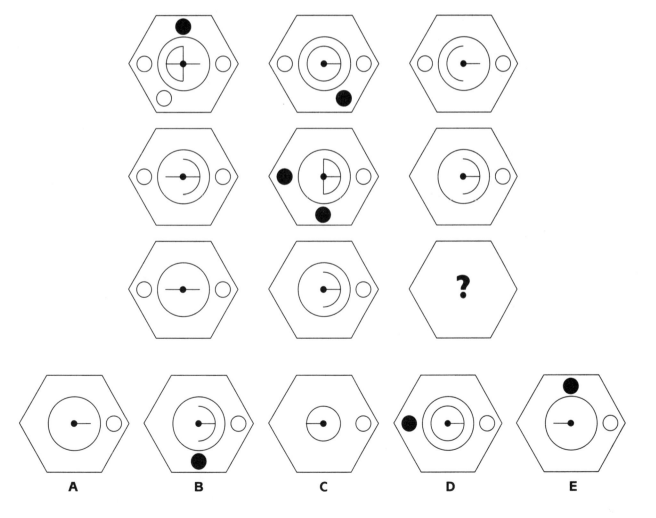

TEST SIX

ANSWERS

1. **A** In the left-hand figure the line at the top right-hand corner disappears. In the right-hand figure the line in the bottom left-hand corner disappears.
2. epilogue, foreword
3. **A** 7649 : 3724 : 888 $76 \times 49 = 3724$
   $37 \times 24 = 888$
4. witty   The rest are synonyms.
5. **D** The diamond moves from the top to the bottom of the triangle. The circle attaches itself to each corner of the triangle in turn, moving anticlockwise.
6. **A** 15   The three numbers in each circle total 100.
7. FERRET: to give ELF, BEE, HER, FAR, ACE DOT.
8. Archibald
9. opulent
10. 1   The numbers of each column from left to right total 25, 23, 21, 19, 17, 15.
11. **C** CASH PIN = spinach. The sports are: snooker (OK SENOR), angling (NIL GANG), karate (A TAKER), tennis (IN NETS)
12. tarry, rush
13. **E** The two rectangles are merged to give the final figure; however, when two circles appear in the same position they are not carried forward to the final figure.
14. **C** 13 $(28 + 37) \div 13 = 5$; $(15 + 29) \div 4 = 11$; $(19 + 33) \div 13 = 4$.
15. maroon
16. 10 $\dfrac{(4 \times 8 \times 3)}{(3 + 4 + 1)} = 12$; $\dfrac{(5 \times 6 \times 4)}{(9 + 2 + 1)} = 10$; $\dfrac{(5 \times 8 \times 5)}{(8 + 6 + 6)} = 10$.
17. CROSS
18. MOBILE
19. OOLONG
20. **B** Each symbol rotates 90° in one direction, then reverses by half that much.
21. RACE
22. FECUND
23. **A** HEAD
24. ANIMOSITY
25. **E**
26. livid, delighted
27. 60 $(7 + 5) \times 4 = 48$; $(6 + 6) \times 6 = 72$; $(8 + 4) \times 5 = 60$.
28. POWERFUL, STALWART
29. infernal, demonic
30. **A** The hexagons in the third row down are obtained by combining the hexagons on the first and second rows, but only similar symbols are carried forward.

TEST SEVEN

QUESTIONS

1. **A**   **B**   **C**   **D**   **E**   **F**   **G**   **H**

   What letter is two to the left of the letter immediately to the right of the letter four to the left of the letter 'F'?

2. I take a certain journey and travel the first half of the complete distance at a speed of 25 mph. How fast would I have to travel over the second half of the journey to average a speed of 50 mph for the whole journey?

   A 50 mph   **B** 60 mph   **C** 100 mph

   D 150 mph   **E** it is impossible

3. 'CHAIR PART' is an anagram of which 9-letter word?

4. Which word in brackets is opposite in meaning to the word in capitals?

   VARIANCE (passivity, venial, fervour, unison, stability)

5. Which is the missing tile?

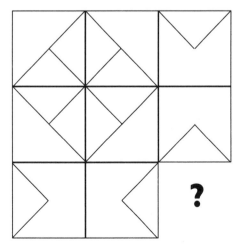

A   **B**   **C**   **D**   **E**

6. What number comes next?

3821, 3949, 4898, 5796, 6493, ?

7. Which two words mean the same?

secret, inviolable, whole, sacred, infallible, intriguing

8. What is the value of: $\frac{3}{5} \div \frac{1}{6}$?

A $2\frac{1}{5}$ **B** $3\frac{1}{5}$ **C** $3\frac{2}{5}$ **D** $\frac{3}{5}$ **E** 4

9. Which of the following is not an anagram of an American president's name?

A   ANTRUM
B   ILL CONN
C   DENY KEN
D   THE CHART
E   CRATER

10. Complete the words reading clockwise. The words are synonyms.

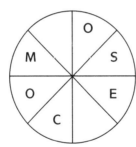

11. Insert in the brackets a word that means the same as the definitions outside the brackets.

part of the head (. . . . . .) holy place

12. Which is the odd one out?

belfry, aisle, font, nave, altar

13.

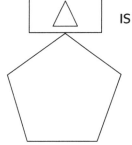 IS TO 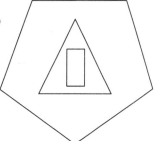 AS 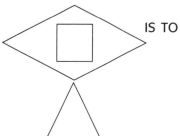 IS TO **?**

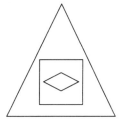

A

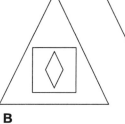

B

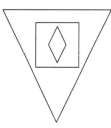

C

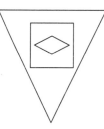

D

E

14.

3	15	9	8
27	7	13	10
46	11	9	36
52	2	26	28

25	16	15	42
9	12	3	2
7	18	12	8
10	31	11	29

Multiply the second-highest odd number in the left-hand grid by the second-lowest even number in the right-hand grid. Is the answer:

A 72   **B** 120   **C** 126   **D** 150 or   **E** 180?

15. Which number should replace the **?**

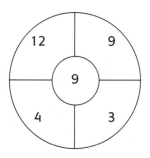

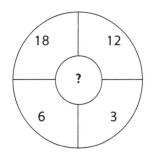

16. Which is the odd one out?

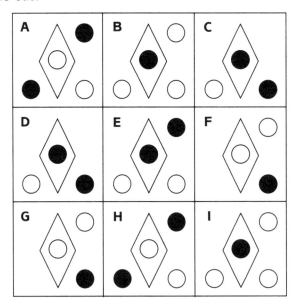

17. Find the one-word anagram.

TENDER NAMES

18. Place a word at the end of the first word to make a new word, and in front of the second word also to make a new word.

CASTOR (. . . . .) PLUM

19. Put in the bracket a word which means the same as the words outside the brackets.

ENCLOSURE (. . .) WRITING IMPLEMENT

20. Which number should replace the **?**

7, 15, 8¾, 9¾, 10½, 4½, **?**

21. What is the name given to a group of WIDGEON?

     A HUTCH
     B MUTE
     C MURDER
     D WEDGE
     E KNOB

22. COMPARISON

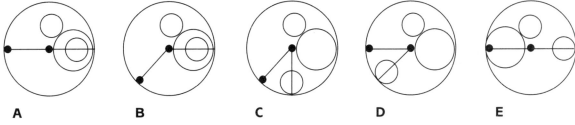

IF ... IS TO ...

THEN ... IS TO ?

A B C D E

23. Place 3 two-letter bits together to equal a 'ROWING BOAT'.

UE   IQ   CA   UE   AS   ID

24. Find a 6-letter word which is make up from these 4 letters only.

SY
AH

25. Which number should replace the ?

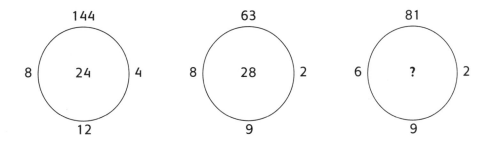

144
8   24   4
12

63
8   28   2
9

81
6   ?   2
9

26. Which of these is the odd one out?

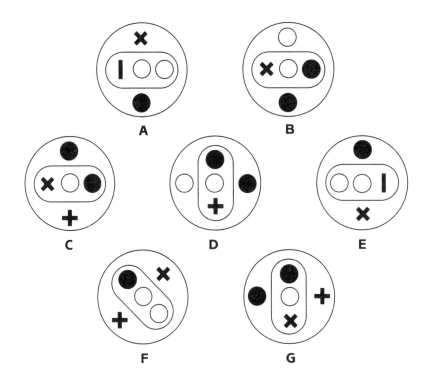

27. Find a word which when placed in front of these words makes new words.

$$(\ldots)$$

. RUNNER
. HOG
. RAGE
. BLOCK
. MAP

28. Find the two words which are synonyms. Both words read clockwise.

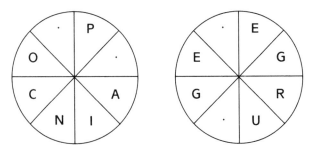

29. Which word means the same as the two words outside the brackets?

affirm (. . . . .) area of a country

30. HEXAGONS
Which hexagon below continues the sequence?

  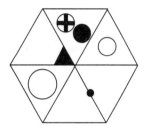 ?

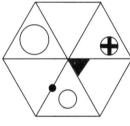 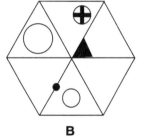

A   B

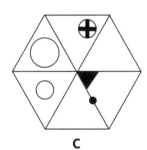 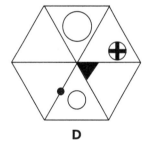 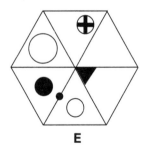

C   D   E

TEST SEVEN

ANSWERS

1. **A**

2. **E** It is impossible. In the first half of the journey you would have used up all the time required to achieve 50 mph average.

3. patriarch

4. unison

5. **A** Looking both across and down, the contents of the third square are determined by the contents of the first two squares, when two lines coincide in the same position, they are not carried forward to the final square.

6. 6887 Reverse last three digits of previous number then add, i.e. 6493 + 394 = 6887.

7. inviolable, sacred

8. **D** $3\frac{3}{5}$ $\frac{3}{5} \div \frac{1}{6} = \frac{3}{5} \times \frac{6}{1} = \frac{18}{5} = 3\frac{3}{5}$

9. **D** THE CHART = Thatcher. The presidents are: Truman (ANTRUM), Lincoln (ILL CONN), Kennedy (DENY KEN), Carter (CRATER).

10. composed, tranquil

11. temple

12. belfry This is outside, on top of the church. The rest are inside on the church floor.

13. **D** The figure at the bottom inverts, increases in size and contains the other two figures (i.e., in this case the triangle). The diamond rotates through 90°, reduces in size and goes inside the square.

14. **B** 120 15 × 8

15. 12 $\frac{12}{4} \times \frac{9}{3} = 9$; $\frac{16}{8} \times \frac{10}{5} = 4$; $\frac{18}{6} \times \frac{12}{3} = 12$.

16. **E** All the others have an identical pairing.

17. ENDEARMENTS

18. SUGAR

19. PEN

20. $12\frac{1}{4}$
    There are 2 series 7, $8\frac{3}{4}$, $10\frac{1}{2}$, $12\frac{1}{4}$ $(+1\frac{3}{4})$
    15, $9\frac{3}{4}$, $4\frac{1}{2}$, $-\frac{3}{4}$ $(-5\frac{1}{4})$

21. **E** KNOB

22. **A**

23. CAIQUE

24. SASHAY

25. 27 $\frac{144}{12} \times \frac{8}{4} = 24$; $\frac{63}{9} \times \frac{8}{2} = 28$; $\frac{81}{9} \times \frac{6}{2} = 27$.

26. **F**

27. ROAD

28. COMPLAIN, BEGRUDGE

29. STATE

30. **E**

TEST EIGHT

QUESTIONS

1. Which option continues the sequence below?

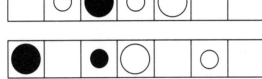

?

A

B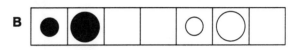

C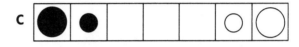

D

E

2. Which of these is not an anagram of the name of a capital city?

    A HASTEN
    B COOL MOB
    C BUN LID
    D LEND NAG
    E IN CASIO

3. What number should replace the question mark?

28		7
	5	
6		37

98		8
	12	
2		22

67		6
	?	
3		14

A 9   **B** 10   **C** 11   **D** 12   **E** 13

4. Which two words are opposite in meaning?

instant, expert, pale, old, exorbitant, fair

5. Which is the odd one out?

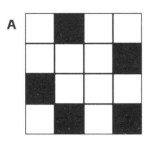 A

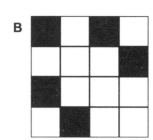 B

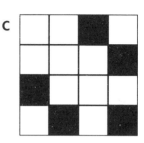 C

 D

 E

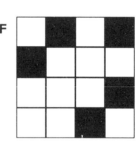 F

6. 4224 : 74
1848 : 38

Which pair of numbers below have the same relationship as that in the two examples above?

A   3624 : 66
B   3656 : 76
C   3818 : 63
D   1224 : 23
E   5412 : 92

7. What creature name is missing from the brackets, reading downwards, to complete the three-letter words?

GE (_)
TO (_)
ME (_)
OA (_)
PI (_)
CO (_)

8.

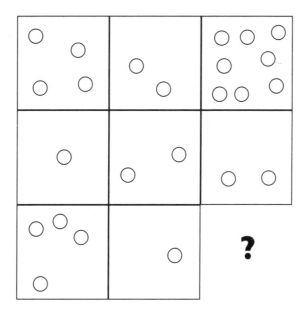

Which is the missing tile?

A   B   C   D   E

9. What number should replace the question mark?

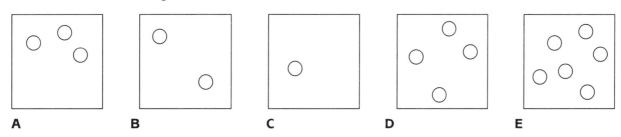

10. 'AN HERETIC' is an anagram of which girl's name?

11. Insert in the brackets a word that means the same as the definitions outside the brackets.

carefree adventure (. . . .) type of bird

12. 7219 : 7938 : 8676

Which set of numbers below has the same relationship as that in the set of numbers above?

      A 4318 : 4712 : 5099
      B 4216 : 4632 : 5064
      C 7684 : 7832 : 8009
      D 2871 : 3004 : 4100
      E 9210 : 9417 : 9988

13. Complete the words reading clockwise. The words are antonyms.

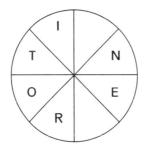
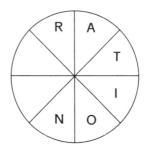

14. Which is the odd one out?

dog, jack, doe, buck, bull

15. Which word in brackets means the same as the word in capitals?

TRIBUTE (explanation, presentation, parody, eulogy, concordat)

16. Place 3 two-letter bits together to equal 'charge with carbon dioxide'.

RA   SE   AE   TA   TE   WI

17. Find a word which when placed on the end of the first word produces a new word and when placed in front of the second word also makes a new word.

HEAVY (. . . . . .) LESS

18. Put in the brackets a word which means the same as the words outside the brackets.

INCITE (. . . . . .) ACT WITH ALACRITY

19. Which number should replace the **?**

19, 23, 29, 31, 37, **?**

20.

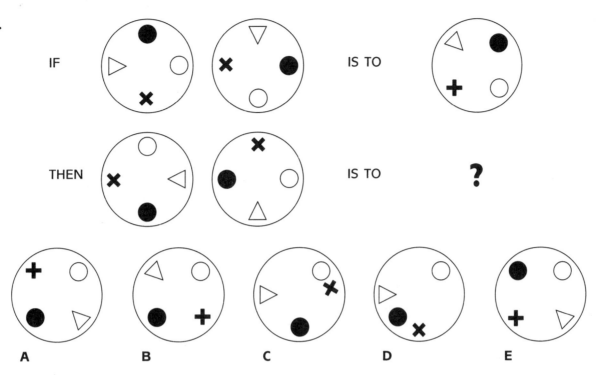

IF ... IS TO ...

THEN ... IS TO ?

A   B   C   D   E

21. Which number should replace the **?**

12, −45, **?**, −632.8125

22. What is the name given to a group of PUPS?

    A RANK
    B LEAP
    C LITTER
    D MORBIDITY
    E RANKLE

23. Find a one-word anagram.

A LONE PET

24. Find the two words which are synonyms. Both words read clockwise.

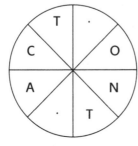
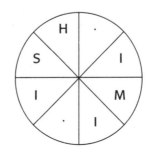

25. Which option below comes next in this sequence?

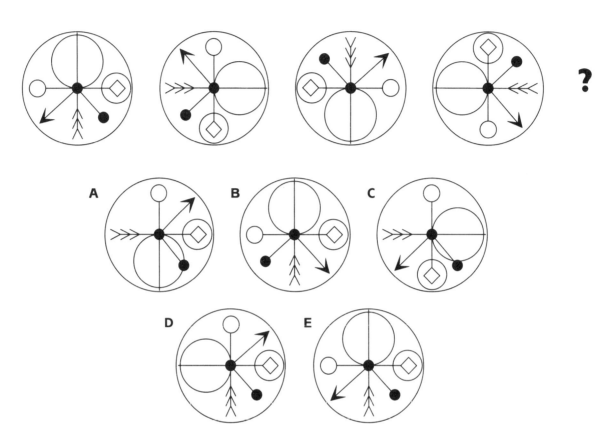

26. Place 2 three-letter bits together to equal the name of sheep.

SHE, INO, WEL, MER, BRI, DIG

27. Which number should replace the ?

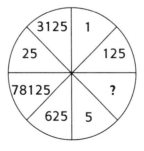

28. Find a 6-letter word which is made up of these 4 letters only.

SA
VL

29. What is a TIRO. Is it:

     A A bird
     B A representative
     C A magnate
     D A novice
     E A collection

30. GRID

Each of the nine squares in the grid marked 1A to 3C, should incorporate all the lines and symbols which are shown in the squares of the same letter and number immediately above and to the left. For example, 2B should incorporate all the lines and symbols that are in 2 and B.

One of the squares is incorrect. Which one is it?

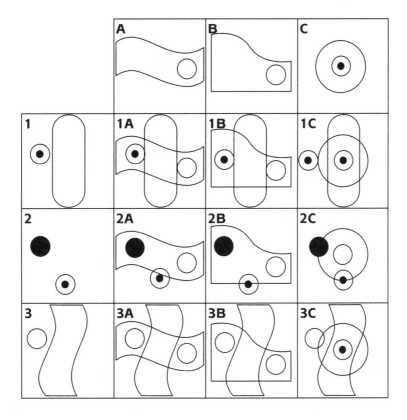

TEST EIGHT

ANSWERS

1. **B** The large black dot moves one forward, two back.
   The small black dot moves two back, one forward.
   The large white circle moves two forward, one back.
   The small white circle moves one back, two forward.

2. **D.** LEND NAG = England. The capital cities are: Athens (HASTEN), Colombo (COOL MOB), Dublin (BUN LID), Nicosia (IN CASIO)

3. **A** 9 $(67 + 14) \div (6 + 3) = 9$

4. exorbitant, fair

5. **B** It is the only one which is not a mirror image of any adjacent squares, either above, below or opposite.

6. **E** 5412 : 92 $54 \div 6 = 9$
   $12 \div 6 = 2$

7. MONKEY. To give GEM, TOO, MEN, OAK, PIE, COY.

8. **D** Looking across, multiply the number of circles in the first two squares to arrive at the number in the third square.
   Looking down, divide the number in the first square by the number in the second square to arrive at the number in the third square.

9. 36 $(43 + 29) \div 2 = 36$

10. Catherine

11. lark

12. **B** 4216 : 4632 : 5064
    $4216 + 416 = 4632 + 432 = 5064$
    You may also have correctly reasoned that there are two series, i.e. from the given model 7219 : 7938 : 8676 there are 72 + 7 = 79 + 7 = 86, and 19 × 2 = 38 × 2 = 76, thus 8676. So the next set of numbers 4216 : 4632 : 5064 gives two series, thus: 42 + 4 = 46 + 4 = 50, and 16 × 2 = 32 × 2 = 64, whence 5064.

13. neurotic, rational

14. doe It is a female animal, the rest are male.

15. eulogy

16. AERATE

17. WEIGHT

18. PROMPT

19. 41 All prime numbers.

20. **A**

21. 168.75 (× −3.75)

22. **C** LITTER

23. ANTELOPE

24. CONTRACT, DIMINISH

25. **E**

26. MERINO

27. 15625 The numbers in the segments, in sequence from lowest to highest, are successively multiplied by 5 : thus, 3125 × 5 = 15625 which in turn × 5 = 78125.

28. VASSAL

29. **D** A novice

30. 2C

TEST NINE

QUESTIONS

1.

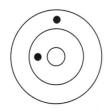 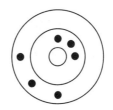

?

What continues the sequence?

 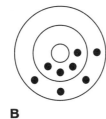 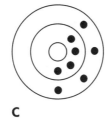 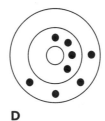 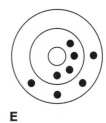

A   **B**   **C**   **D**   **E**

2. Complete the words reading clockwise. The words are synonyms.

 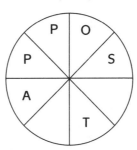

3. In a game for 14 players that lasts exactly 70 minutes there are 6 reserves that alternate equally with each player. This means that all players, including reserves are on the pitch for the same amount of time exactly. For how long?

     A   38 mins   **B**   42 mins   **C**   49 mins

     D   55 mins   **E**   59 mins

4. 'DEEP PAGAN' is an anagram of which 9-letter word?

5. Which is the odd one out?

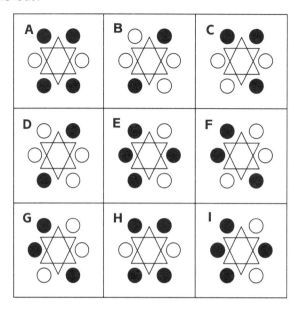

6. What number should replace the question mark?

18	6	15	9
13	11	7	17
5	19	**?**	3
16	8	14	10

7. TRIANGLE : ISOSCELES

Choose the pair that best expresses a relationship similar to that of the pair above.

A rectangle   : square
B pentagon   : hexagon
C circle   : diameter
D rhombus   : polygon
E quadrilateral : trapezium

8. Insert in the brackets a word that means the same as the definitions outside the brackets.

natural harbour (. . .) howl

9. Into which of the boxes on the right can a dot be placed so that both dots then meet the same conditions as in the box on the left?

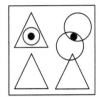 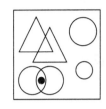  

        A   **B**   **C**   **D**   **E**

10. What number should replace the question mark?

		31	
	22		42
13			
	?		

11. Which is the odd one out?

chain, fret, hack, jig, pitch

12. Which two words are closest in meaning?

plaudit, cliché, outfit, rostrum, tablet, platitude

13. What comes next?

0.25, 0.3, 0.4, 0.55, **?**

14. Which one of these is not an anagram of a country name?

A   BOIL VIA
B   RACE DUO
C   INCA SPA
D   FLAN DIN
E   I REGAIN

15. Which word in brackets is opposite in meaning to the word in capitals?

INERTIA (tolerance, vigour, flexibility, strength, indolence)

16. Which number should replace the **?**

$$13, 1, 10\frac{1}{2}, 3\frac{1}{4}, 8, 5\frac{1}{2}, ?$$

17. Put in the brackets a word which means the same as the words outside the brackets.

CONUNDRUM (. . . . . .) SIEVE

18. Find a word which when added on to the end of the first word makes a new word, and when placed in front of the second word also means a new word.

TIGER (. . . .) PAD

19. Find the one-word anagram.

LET MAN LOVE

20. Which circle continues the sequence?

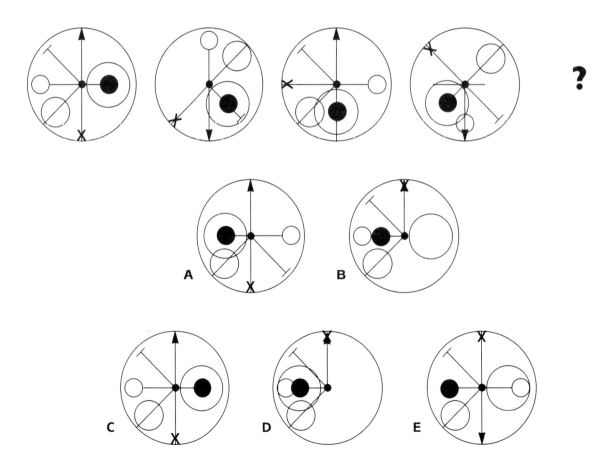

21. Which number should replace the **?**

24, 28, 36, –42, 54, 63, ?

22. What is the name given to a group of STARLINGS?

A CHASE
B MURMURATION
C BROOD
D HEAD
E TIDING

23. Find a 6-letter word which is made up from these 4 letters only.

WE
HZ

24. Place 3 two-letter bits together to make an 'ELK'.

TI   DE   WA   RE   PI   CO

25. HEXAGONS
Which hexagon below continues the sequence?

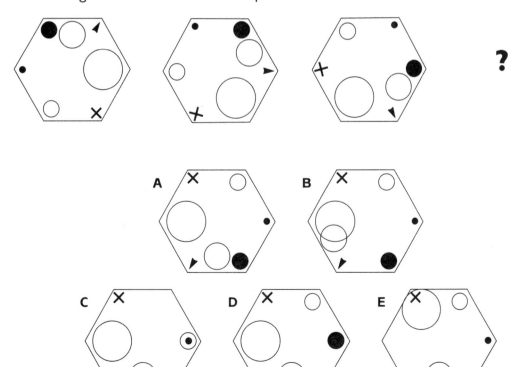

26. Find a word which when placed in front of each of these words makes new words.

. BALL

. SHAKE

(. . . .)   . STAND

. CREAM

. RAIL

27. What is a FULMAR. Is it:

A   A bird

B   A fish

C   An animal

D   A reptile

E   An insect

28. Find two words which are SYNONYMS. Both words read clockwise.

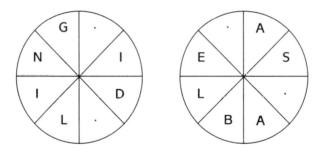

29. Place two 3-letter bits together to equal the name of a bone of the body

CYX, HUM, TIB, ROC, IAL, COC, RUS

30. SYMBOLS

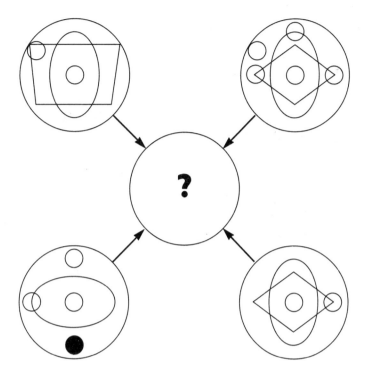

Each line and symbol which appears in the four outer circles above is transferred to the centre circle according to these rules:

If a line or symbol occurs in the outer circles

once:	it is transferred
twice:	it is possibly transferred
3 times:	it is transferred
4 times:	it is not transferred

Which of the circles A, B, C, D or E shown below should appear at the centre of the diagram above?

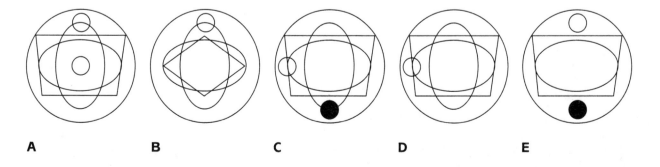

A   B   C   D   E

TEST NINE

ANSWERS

1. **E** The dot in the outer circle moves 45° anticlockwise each time and a further dot is added.
   The dot in the inner circle moves 45° clockwise each time and a further dot is added.
2. relevant, apposite
3. **C** 49 mins $\dfrac{70 \times 14}{20} = 49$ mins
4. appendage
5. **C** Each of the others has an identical pairing.
6. 21 Reading across, the first pair of numbers and the second pair of numbers total 24.
7. **E** quadrilateral : trapezium. Isosceles is a type of triangle; trapezium is a type of quadrilateral.
8. bay
9. **B** so that the small circle, the triangle and both large circles contain a dot.
10. 24 each number describes its position in the grid, i.e., 24 = 2 lines across, 4 lines down.
11. pitch This is a type of fork; the others are types of saw.
12. cliché, platitude
13. 0.75 Add 0.05, 0.1, 0.15, 0.2.
14. **C** INCA SPA = Caspian. The countries are: Bolivia (BOIL VIA), Ecuador (RACE DUO), Finland (FLAN DIN), Nigeria (I REGAIN).
15. vigour
16. 5½ There are 2 series: 13, 10½, 8, 5½ (–2½) 1, 3¼, 5½, 7¾ (+2¼).
17. RIDDLE
18. LILY
19. MALEVOLENT
20. **D**
21. 81 There are 2 series: 24, 36, 54, 81 (× 1½) and 28, –42, 63, –94½ (x–1½)
22. **B** MURMURATION
23. WHEEZE
24. WAPITI
25. **A**
26. HAND
27. **A** a bird
28. MIDDLING, PASSABLE
29. COCCYX
30. **C**

TEST TEN

QUESTIONS

1.

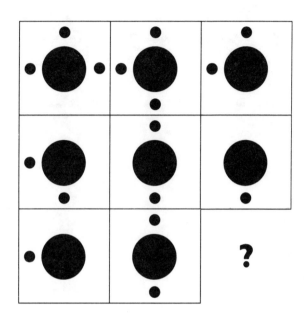

Which tile is missing?

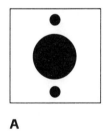    

A   **B**   **C**   **D**   **E**

2. Which of the following is not an anagram of a type of building?

        A   DO A GAP
        B   SUE MUM
        C   EAR GAG
        D   WINO BAR
        E   PELMET

3.

42	15	14
56	35	8
36	?	4

What number is missing?

4. Which two words are opposite in meaning?

strength, modesty, dread, control, mood, conceit

5. **A**   **B**   **C**   **D**   **E**   **F**   **G**   **H**

What letter is three to the right of the letter immediately to the left of the letter two to the right of the letter 'B'?

6.

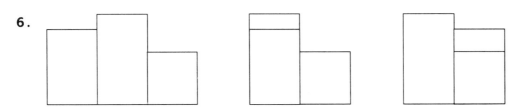

What comes next in the above sequence?

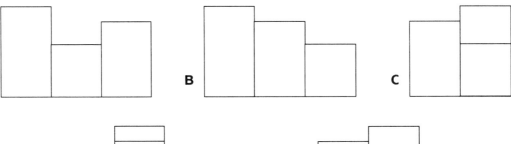

7. Complete the words reading clockwise. The words are antonyms.

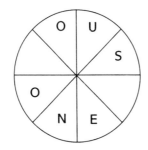 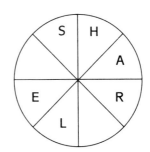

8. 78214, 57498, 37490, **?**

What comes next?

A 18742   **B** 22470   **C** 26890   **D** 42628   **E** 46832

9. 'halt Annie' is an anagram of which boy's name?

10. Which word in brackets is closest in meaning to the word in capitals?

TESTIMONY (speech, deposition, proxy, decision, epithet)

11. Which is the odd one out?

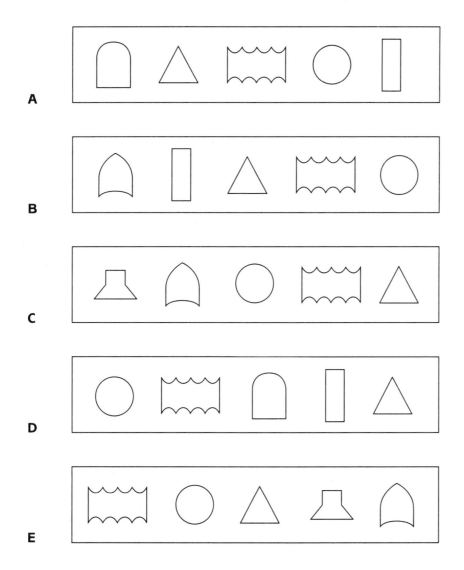

A

B

C

D

E

12. 486542 is to 395633 as 748356 is to:

        A 659447
        B 839467
        C 839265
        D 657447
        E 932146

13. Insert in the brackets a word that means the same as the definitions outside the brackets.

hire (. . . .) tear

14. Which is the odd one out?

frangipane, Garibaldi, madeleine, angel, savarin

15. 5476 : 74

Which pair of numbers below have the same relationship as that of the numbers above?

        A 3812 : 23
        B 5419 : 59
        C 7225 : 85
        D 3821 : 64
        E 8569 : 92

16. Find the one-word anagram.

AFRICAN LION

17. Put in the brackets a word which means the same as the words outside the brackets.

ROB (. . . . .) GUN

18. Which number should replace the **?**

1, 12, 3½, 9½, 6, 7, ?

19. Find a word which when placed on the end of the first word makes a new word, and when placed in front of the second word also makes a new word.

CAVE (. . .) KIND

20. Which is the odd one out?

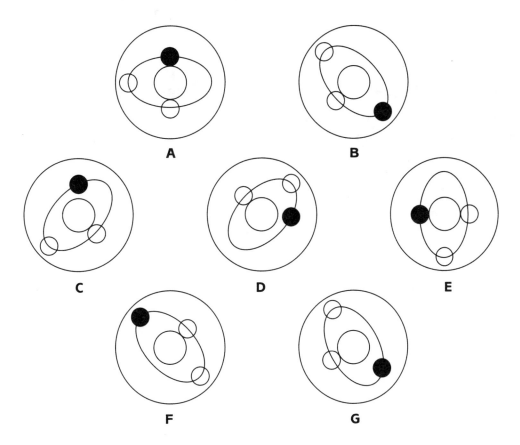

21. Which is the odd one out?

      A   MAXIMUM
      B   GODETIA
      C   THEODOLITE
      D   ATTACKER
      E   STARLIGHT

22. What is the name given to a group of PHEASANT?

      A   PUDDLE
      B   SWATCH
      C   GAM
      D   NIDE
      E   GAGGLE

23. Place 3 two-letter bits together to equal 'WHITE CLAY'.

OL   DI   KA   NO   IN   SP

24. Find a 6-letter word which is made up of these 4 letters only.

CYIL

25. HEXAGON

Which hexagon fits the missing space?

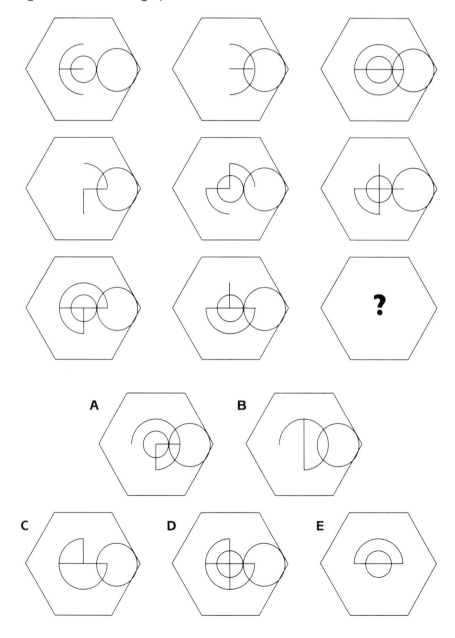

26. Which number should replace the ?

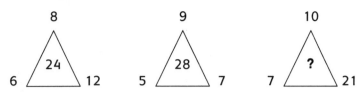

27. Find the two words which are synonyms. Both words read clockwise.

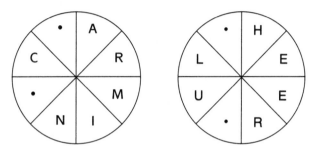

28. Find a word which when placed in front of these words makes new words.

(. . . .)

. LIGHT
. VALVE
. GAP
. WATCH
. PRESS

29. What is the name given to a group of LEOPARDS?

A LEPE
B COLONY
C GATHERING
D POUCH
E FRINGE

30. SYMBOLS

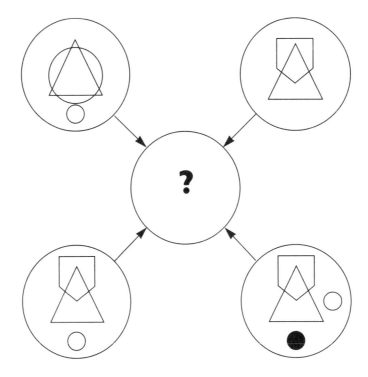

Each line and symbol which appears in the four outer circles above is transferred to the centre circle according to these rules:

If a line or symbol occurs in the outer circles

once:	it is transferred
twice:	it is possibly transferred
3 times:	it is transferred
4 times:	it is not transferred

Which of the circles A, B, C, D or E shown below should appear at the centre of the diagram above?

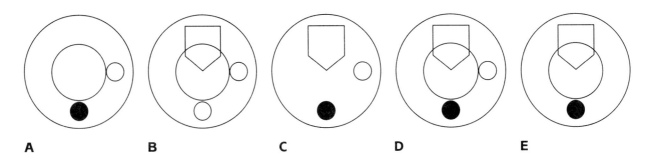

A   B   C   D   E

TEST TEN

ANSWERS

1. **D** Looking both across and down, only parts which are common to the first two squares are carried forward to the third square.

2. **D** WINO BAR = rainbow. The buildings are: pagoda (DO A GAP), museum (SUE MUM), garage (EAR GAG), temple (PELMET)

3. 45 $36 \div 4 \times 5$

4. modesty, conceit

5. **F**

6. **A** The medium-size rectangle which starts on the far left moves to the far right one stage at a time.

7. venomous, harmless

8. **B** 22470 3×7490

9. Nathaniel

10. deposition

11. **B** 'A' contains the same figures as 'D' 'C' contains the same figures as 'E'

12. **D** 657447

7	4	8	3	5	6
−1	+1	−1	+1	−1	+1
6	5	7	4	4	7

13. rent

14. Garibaldi This is a biscuit; the rest are cakes.

15. 7225 : 85   85 is the square root of 7225.

16. CALIFORNIAN

17. RIFLE

18. 8½ There are 2 series: 1, 3½, 6, 8½ (+2½) 12, 9½, 7, 4½ (−2½)

19. MAN

20. D

21. MAXIMUM All of the other words contain an animal name spelled backwards.

22. **D** NIDE

23. KAOLIN

24. CYCLIC

25. **B** The medium-sized circle on the right of the hexagons is common to all hexagons including B. In all other instances, the first and second horizontal rows are merged to produce the third row and similar symbols disappear.

26. 63 $(8 − 6) \times 12 = 24$; $(9 − 5) \times 7 = 28$; $(10 − 7) \times 21 = 63$.

27. CHARMING, CHEERFUL

28. STOP

29. A LEPE

30. D

TEST ELEVEN

QUESTIONS

1. What creature name should be placed in the brackets, reading downwards to complete the three-letter words?

    DE (_)
    AT (_)
    PE (_)
    HA (_)
    HU (_)
    OI (_)

2. What number should replace the question mark?

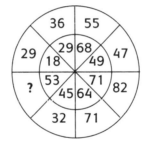

3.

    What continues the above sequence?

A

B

C

D

E

4.

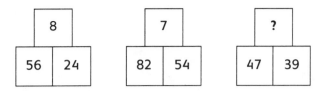

What number should replace the question mark?

A 2   **B** 4   **C** 6   **D** 8   **E** 9

5. Which of the following is not an anagram of a composer's name?

> **A** PHONIC
> **B** GNAWER
> **C** HAD LEN
> **D** IS IRONS
> **E** MET BACH

6. Insert in the brackets a word that means the same as the definitions outside the brackets

> longing or desire (. . .) monetary unit

7. Complete the words reading clockwise. The words are antonyms.

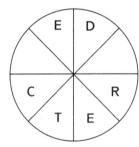 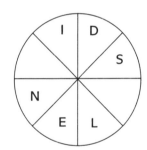

8. What comes next?

> 40812, 32480, 15360, **?**

9. 'her tactic' is an anagram of which 9-letter word?

10. Which word in brackets is opposite in meaning to the word in capitals?

> LIMPID (airy, opaque, sour, viable, lucid)

11. Which is the odd one out?

> tibia, patella, femur, humerus, fibula

12. Which is the odd one out?

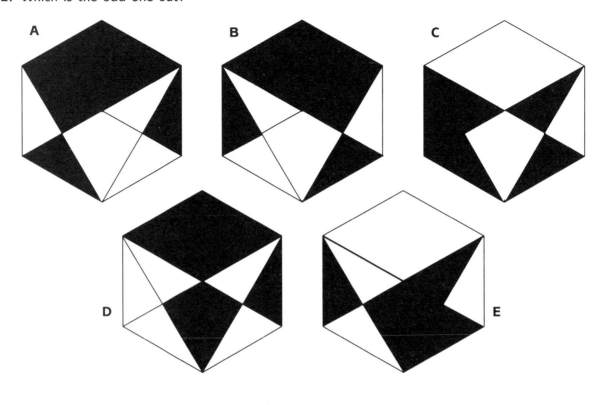

13.

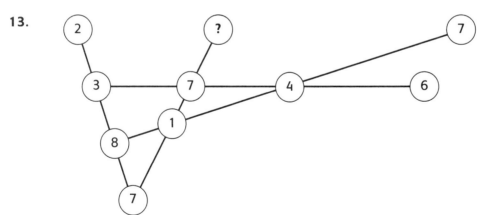

What number is missing from the top circle?

14. Which word in brackets is closest in meaning to the word in capitals?

INGENUOUS (honest, shrewd, flattering, congenital, shy)

15.

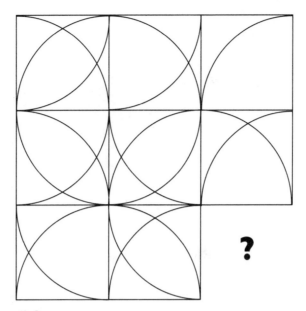

Which is the missing tile?

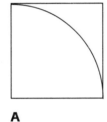 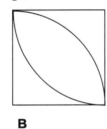 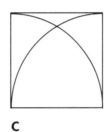 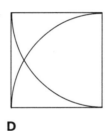 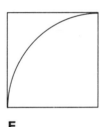

A   **B**   **C**   **D**   **E**

16. Find a 6-letter word which is made up from these 4 letters only.

AY
BN

17. Put a word in the brackets which means the same as the words outside the brackets

DEER (. . .) FISH EGGS

18. Find a word which when placed on the end of the first word makes a new word, and when placed in front of the second word also makes a new word.

PACK (. . .) CREAM

19. Which number should replace the **?**

26, –19.5, **?** –10.96875

20. Insert a word which means the same as the two words outside the brackets.

NURSE EGGS (. . . . .) ENGRAVE

21. GRID

   Each of the nine squares in the grid marked 1A to 3C, should incorporate all the lines and symbols which are shown in the squares of the same letter and number immediately above and to the left. For example, 2B should incorporate all the lines that are in 2 and B.
   One of the squares is incorrect. Which one is it?

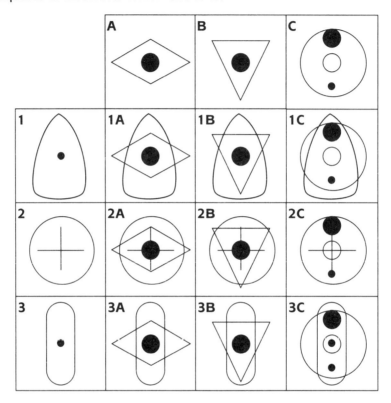

22. Place 3 two-letter bits together to make an 'ISLAND'.

   NI   LI   BI   SI   KI   TI

23. What is the name given to a group of ASSES?

   A   SPRING
   B   KENNEL
   C   HAND
   D   MAGNITUDE
   E   PACE

24. Which number should replace the **?**

   17, 36, 20½, 30½, 24, 25, **?**

25. HEXAGONS

Which hexagon below continues the sequence?

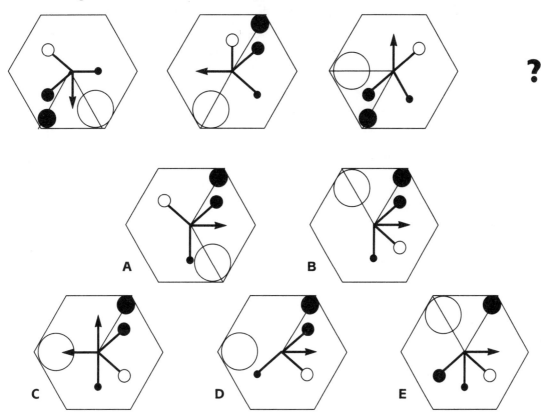

26. Insert a word which completes the first word and commences the second word

NEWS (. . . . .) ROUND

27. Find the two words which are SYNONYMS. Both words read anti-clockwise.

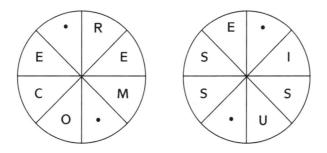

28. Find the one-word anagram.

MEAT IS ON IT

29. Which is the odd word out?

    A BADING
    B FLEEING
    C DOCTOR
    D SAPPHIRE
    E LANYARD

30. SYMBOLS

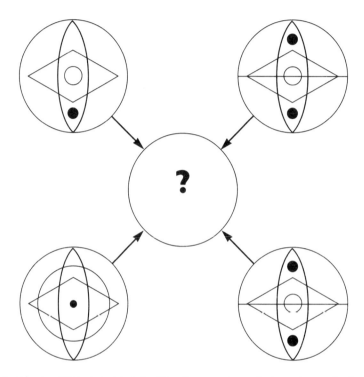

Each line and symbol which appears in the four outer circles above is transferred to the centre according to these rules:

If a line or symbol occurs in the outer circles

        once: it is transferred
        twice: it is possibly transferred
        3 times: it is transferred
        4 times: it is not transferred

Which of the circles A, B, C, D or E shown below should appear at the centre of the diagram above?

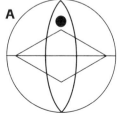 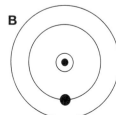 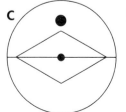 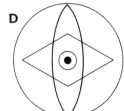 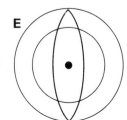

TEST ELEVEN

ANSWERS

1. WEASEL   to give DEW, ATE, PEA, HAS, HUE, OIL
2. 51 Alternate numbers in every opposite segment total 100.
3. **D**   The top arm moves 45° anticlockwise at each stage. The bottom arm moves 45° clockwise at each stage.
4. **A** 2 $47 - 39 \div 4 = 2$
5. **E**   MET BACH = Macbeth.
   The composers are: Chopin (PHONIC), Wagner (GNAWER), Handel (HAD LEN), Rossini (IS IRONS).
6. yen
7. wretched, splendid
8. 5400 15×360
9. architect
10. opaque
11. humerus   This is an arm bone; the rest are leg bones.
12. **B**   A is the same as E with black/white reversal.
    C is the same as D with black/white reversal.
13. **5**   Each line of 4 connected circles totals 20.
14. honest
15. **A**   Looking across and down, any lines common to the first two squares are not carried forward to the third square.
16. BANYAN
17. ROE
18. ICE
19. 14.625 ($\times -.75$)
20. HATCH
21. 1C
22. BIKINI
23. E PACE
24. 27½   There are 2 series: 17, 20½, 24, 27½ (+3½) and 36, 30½, 25, 19½, (−5½)
25. **B**
26. PAPER
27. COMMERCE, BUSINESS
28. ESTIMATION
29. **D** SAPPHIRE   All of the other words have the name of a fish spelled backwards within them.
30. **B**

TEST TWELVE

QUESTIONS

1.

Which is the missing segment?

A   B   C   D   E

2. 1836 : 3654 : 5472

Which set of numbers below have the same relationship to each other as the three numbers above?

A   5913 : 7832 : 9751
B   3627 : 5445 : 7623
C   6484 : 4262 : 2040
D   4829 : 5918 : 6007
E   1634 : 3821 : 5648

3. JERKIN : JACKET

Choose the pair that best expresses a relationship similar to the pair above.

A	cagoule	: dress
B	mantilla	: scarf
C	dolman	: hat
D	halter	: scarf
E	cummerbund	: neckerchief

4. Which two words are closest in meaning?

ill-mannered, obtrusive, covert, calm, nosy, odd

5. Complete the words reading clockwise. The words are synonyms.

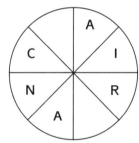 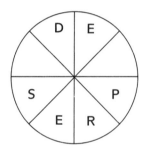

6. A man returns from his orchard with a small bag of apples. To his first neighbour he gives half the apples plus half an apple, to his second he gives half what he had left plus half an apple and to the third he gives half what he had left plus half an apple. That meant he had no apples left. How many apples did his first neighbour receive?

7. 'lime Clint' is an anagram of which girl's name?

8.

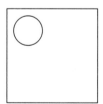 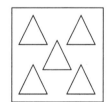 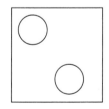 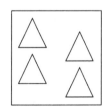 **?**

What comes next in the above sequence?

A **B** 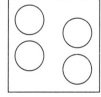 **C** 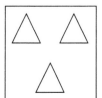 **D** 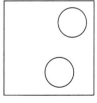 **E**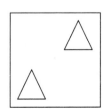

9.   Insert in the brackets a word that means the same as the definitions outside the brackets.

pelvis (. . .) fruit of the rose

10.   5639 : 1112 : 23

Which set of numbers below have the same relationship to each other as that in the set of numbers above?

A   7492 :   168 : 96
B   6858 : 1413 : 54
C   3517 : 1029 : 33
D   2962 :   426 : 13
E   7995 : 1614 : 57

11.   Which is the odd one out?

pastoral, bucolic, urban, rustic, rural

12.   Which two words are opposite in meaning?

reproof, forsake, praise, agree, despise, mitigate

13.   Which is the odd one out?

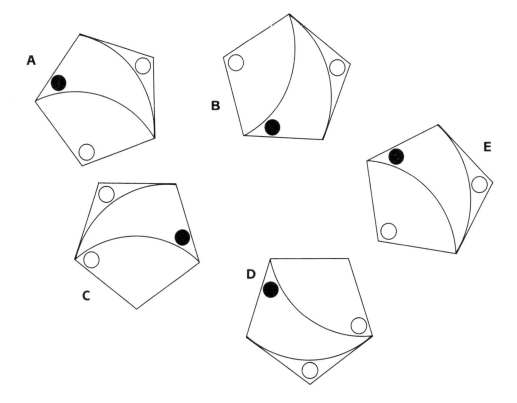

14.

7	13	25	36
18	27	9	24
15	22	12	11

7	8	5	18
3	12	19	9
16	10	14	2

Multiply the third-highest odd number in the left-hand grid by the second-lowest even number in the right-hand grid.

15. Which of the following is not an anagram of an animal name?

    A   TEACH HE
    B   HEN TRAP
    C   FA GRIEF
    D   PALE ROD
    E   MUD RATS

16. Find a 6-letter word which is made up of these 4 letters only.

AS
EB

17. Put in the brackets a word which means the same as the words outside the brackets.

WINDOW (. . . .) STRIP OF MATERIAL

18. Find a word which when added to the first word makes a new word, and when placed in the front of the second word also makes a new word.

MANTEL (. . . . .) MEAL

19. What is the name given to a group of MARTENS?

    A   RICHESSE
    B   OBSERVATION
    C   KINDLE
    D   RUSH
    E   COVEY

20. GRID

Each of the nine squares marked 1A to 3C should incorporate all the lines and symbols which are shown in the squares A, B or C and 1, 2 or 3, directly to the left and directly above. Thus 2B should incorporate all the lines and symbols in 2 and B.

One of the squares, 1A to 3C, is incorrect.

Which one is it?

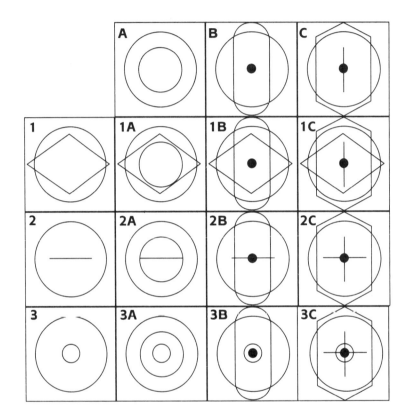

21. Which word can be inserted between the brackets to mean the same as those outside?

MÊLÉE (. . . .) BECOME JAGGED

22. Find the two words which are SYNONYMS. Both words read clockwise.

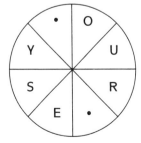 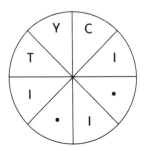

23. Find 3 two-letter bits to equal 'SUBSTITUTE'.

SA   ER   MO   KI   TZ   TS

24. Which number should replace the **?**

17, 88, 176, 847, 1595, **?**

25. HEXAGONS
Which hexagon below continues the sequence?

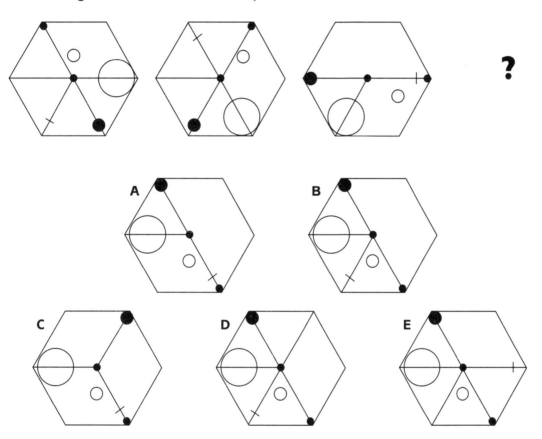

26. Which word means the opposite of ORIENTAL?

      A   NORTHERN
      B   SOUTHERN
      C   FOREIGN
      D   ISLANDER
      E   OCCIDENTAL

27. SYMBOLS

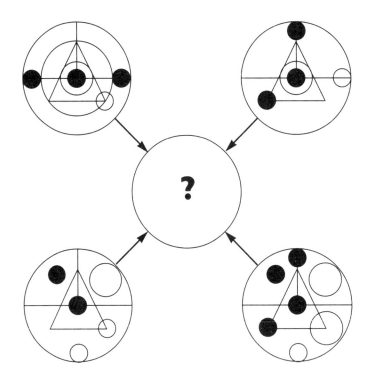

Each line and symbol which appears in the four outer circles above is transferred to the centre circle according to these rules:

If a line or symbol occurs in the outer circles

once:	it is transferred
twice:	it is possibly transferred
3 times :	it is transferred
4 times :	it is not transferred

Which of the circles A, B, C, D or E shown below should appear at the centre of the diagram above?

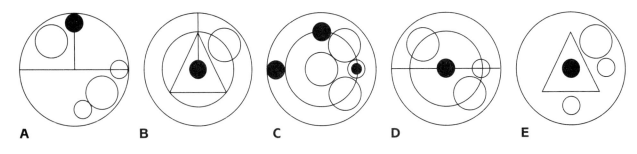

A   B   C   D   E

28. Which number should replace the ?

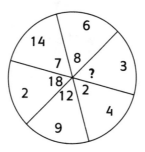

29. Find the one-word anagram.

HORNS OR ICE

30. Place 2 three-letter bits together to equal the name of a FISH.

PER, COD, PLA, SOL, ECE, KIP

TEST TWELVE

ANSWERS

1. **D** Each segment is a mirror image of the segment opposite, but with black and white reversal.

2. **B** 3627 : 5445 : 7263
   3 6 2 7
   +2 −2 +2 −2
   5 4 4 5
   +2 −2 +2 −2
   7 2 6 3

3. **B** mantilla : scarf

4. obtrusive, nosy

5. chairman, presider

6. 4   to the first   3½ + ½ = 4, leaving 3; to the second   1½ + ½ = 2, leaving 1; to the third   ½ + ½ = 1, leaving none.

7. Millicent

8. **A** There are two alternate sequences. The first, starting with one circle increases by one circle each time. The second, starting with five triangles, decreases by one triangle each time.

9. hip

10. **B** 6858 : 1413 : 54
    6 + 8 = 14; 5 + 8 = 13
        1 + 4 = 5; 1 + 3 = 4

11. urban. This relates to towns; the rest relate to countryside.

12. reproof, praise

13. **B** 'A' and 'E' are the same rotated. 'C' and 'D' are the same rotated.

14. 120   15 × 8

15. **E** MUD RATS = mustard. The animals are: cheetah (TEACH HE), panther (HEN TRAP), giraffe (FA GRIEF), leopard (PALE ROD)

16. ABBESS

17. SASH

18. PIECE

19. **A** RICHESSE

20. 3C

21. FRAY

22. COURTESY, CIVILITY

23. ERSATZ

24. 7546   Each number is reversed and added to the previous number.

25. **B**

26. **E** OCCIDENTAL

27. **C**

28. 27   (3 × 18) = (2 × 27)

29. RHINOCEROS

30. KIPPER

TEST THIRTEEN

QUESTIONS

1. Complete the words reading clockwise. The words are antonyms.

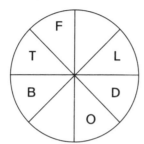 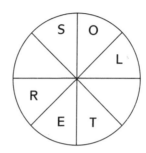

2. What number should replace the question mark?

8
11
14

11
?
23

13
22
31

3. 'sham mince' is an anagram of which 9-letter word?

4. Which two words are closest in meaning?

    European, French, native, Gallic, Irish, Italian

5. Which number is the odd one out?

    A   36119
    B   84129
    C   25616
    D   48418
    E   52923

6. **A**   **B**   **C**   **D**   **E**   **F**   **G**   **H**

    What letter is two to the right of the letter three to the left of the letter immediately to the right of the letter 'C'?

7. Insert in the brackets a word that means the same as the definitions outside the brackets.

    bad tempered (. . . .) average

8. 368 (144108) 439
    749 (252120) 564
    835 (?)   298

    What number is missing from the brackets?

9.

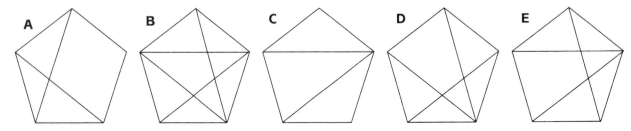

    Which is the missing pentagon?

10. Which of the following is not an anagram of a flower name?

           A   A BIG EON
           B   AIR PLUM
           C   COLE CAR
           D   THE HARE
           E   IF A SUCH

11.

7	9	?	51
2	11	?	82

Which is missing?

16	22	20	20	18
13	33	33	31	30
A	**B**	**C**	**D**	**E**

12.

What continues the above sequence?

  A   **B**   **C**   **D**   **E**

13. Which is the odd one out?

        fiery, impetuous, reckless, angry, volatile

14. Which two words are opposite in meaning?

        delightful, hostile, hopeless, congenial, puny, curt

15. HONEST is to false as

OFFEND is to (insult, present, give, please, serve)

16. Which number should replace the **?**

8	10	3	14
7	14	5	21
9	11	4	25
6	17	8	?

17. Find a word which when placed on the end of the first word makes a new word and when placed in front of the second word also makes a new word.

TONIC (. . . . .) FALL

18. Find the one-word anagram.

THE ACHE

19. Put in the brackets a word which means the same as the words outside the brackets.

INTENSE (. . . . .) MUSICAL NOTE

20. Find a 6-letter word which is made up of these 4 letters only.

TD
OE

21. Find 3 two-letter bits to equal 'LOZENGE'

CH   IL   CA   SA   OU   ME

22. What is the name given to a group of TEAL?

A SPRING
B NYE
C PRIDE
D BADELYNGE
E BURY

23. COMPARISON

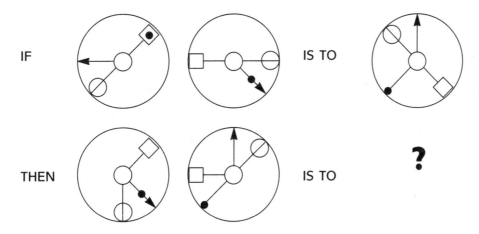

IF ... IS TO

THEN ... IS TO ... **?**

A   B   C   D   E

24. How many packets can be placed in the crate?

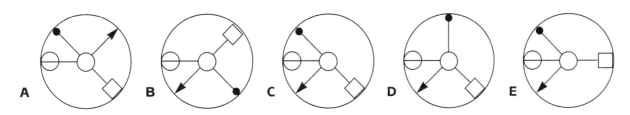

1.680 m × 1.200 m × 1.400 m

.420 m × .060 × .070 m

25. Find a word which when placed in front of each of these words makes new words.

(. . . .)

. PATH
. WEAR
. FAULT
. FALL
. PAD

26. Place 3 two-letter bits together to equal a boy's name.

RT, AU, GE, BE, IN, RU, IE

27. HEXAGONS
    Which hexagon below continues the sequence?

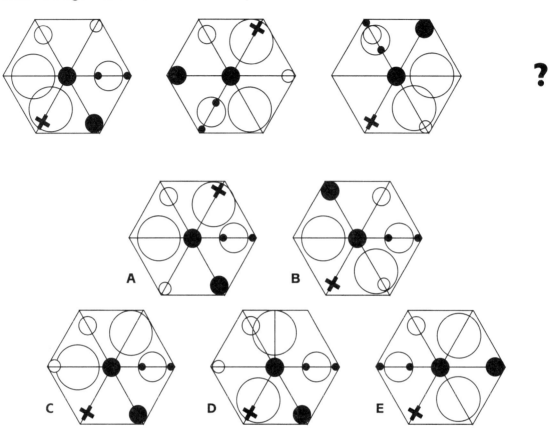

28. Find the two words which are SYNONYMS. One word reads clockwise, the other anticlockwise.

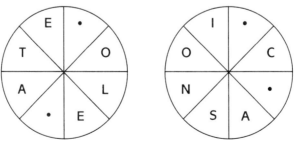

29. Which word in the brackets means the same as the words outside?

AN ANIMAL (. . . .) COURT FAVOUR

30. SYMBOLS

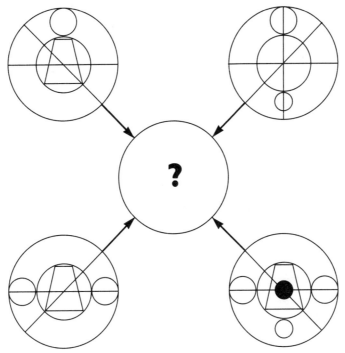

Each line and symbol which appears in the four outer circles above is transferred to the centre circle according to these rules:

If a line or symbol occurs in the outer circles

        once: it is transferred
        twice: it is possibly transferred
        3 times: it is transferred
        4 times: it is not transferred

Which of the circles A, B, C, D or E shown below should appear at the centre of the diagram above?

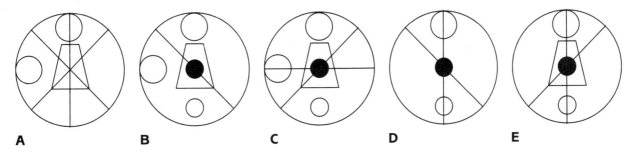

A   **B**   **C**   **D**   **E**

TEST THIRTEEN

ANSWERS

1. doubtful, resolute
2. 17   Reading down column 1, the figures increase +3 each time, column 2 is +6 and column 3, +9.
3. mechanism
4. French, Gallic
5. **D** 48418   All the rest consist of a square number followed by its square root.
6. **C**
7. mean
8. 120144 $8 \times 3 \times 5 = 120$
   $2 \times 9 \times 8 = 144$
9. **E**   The contents of each pentagon are determined by the contents of the two pentagons immediately below it. When two lines appear in the same position in these two pentagons, they do not appear in the pentagon above it.
10. **C**   COLE CAR = coracle. The flowers are: begonia (A BIG EON), primula (AIR PLUM), heather (THE HARE), fuchsia (IF A SUCH).
11. **D** $7 + 2 = 9$ $2 + 9 = 11$
    $9 + 11 = 20$ $11 + 20 = 31$, etc.
12. **B**   At each stage the outer arc moves 90° anticlockwise, the middle arc moves 90° clockwise and the inner arc moves 90° clockwise.
13. angry   The rest are synonyms.
14. hostile, congenial
15. please (antonyms)
16. 31 $(8 \times 3) - 10 = 14$;
    $(7 \times 5) - 14 = 21$; $(9 \times 4) - 11 = 25$;
    $(6 \times 8) - 17 = 31$.
17. WATER
18. CHEETAH
19. SHARP
20. TOOTED, DOTTED
21. CACHOU
22. **A** SPRING
23. **C**
24. 1600
25. FOOT
26. BERTIE
27. **A**
28. TOLERATE, SANCTION
29. FAWN
30. **E**

TEST FOURTEEN

QUESTIONS

1. Which is the odd one out?

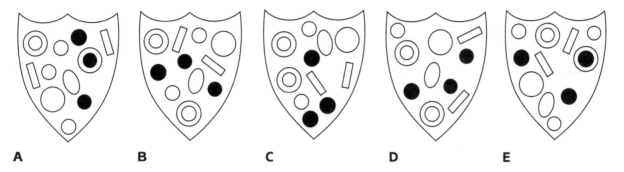

A   B   C   D   E

2. 'nice shirt' is an anagram of which girl's name?

3. Which number should replace the question mark?

5	9	6	10
8	12	9	13
4	8	5	9
7	11	8	?

4. GENTIAN : BLUE

    Choose the pair that best expresses a relationship similar to that of the pair above.

    A citron   : green
    B bisque : brown
    C jade   : black
    D saffron : grey
    E cinnabar : red

5. Which word in brackets is opposite in meaning to the word in capitals?

    VIGILANT (panicky, cool, stupid, feeble, remiss)

6. Complete the words reading clockwise. The words are synonyms.

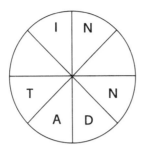 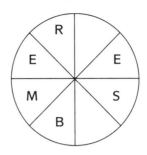

7. Identify a number in the grid which meets the
   two following simple rules:
   1. It is not in any line across which contains a
   square number.
   2. It is not in any line down which contains a prime number.

25	22	15	19
29	7	18	32
14	4	27	26
2	39	16	12

8. What comes next?

   **?**

A    B   C

D   E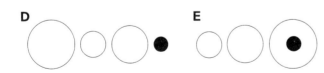

9. Which of the following is not an anagram of a fruit name?

   A AN OGRE
   B RIP COAT
   C MINK PUP
   D RAN PIPS
   E DAMN RAIN

10. 7341 : 5904
6812 : 4626

Which pair of numbers below have the same relationship as that in the two examples above?

A 4593 : 6482
B 6482 : 4593
C 7142 : 3817
D 4819 : 2336
E 3811 : 2628

11. Which two words mean the same?

seal, sieve, purify, colander, diary, search

12.

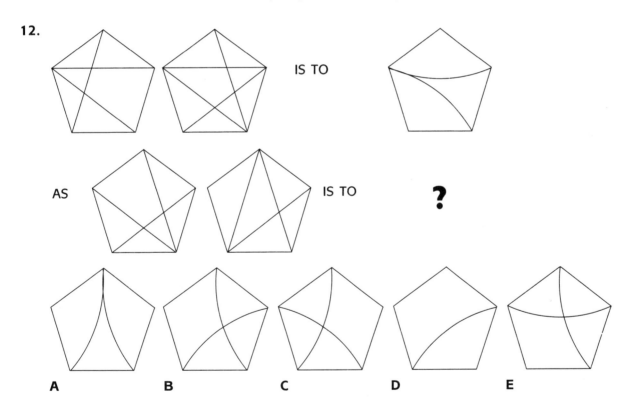

13. Which is the odd one out?

brae, dingle, coomb, corrie, glen

14. Insert in the brackets a word that means the same as the definitions outside the brackets.

walk with quick soft steps (. . . . . .) glib rapid speech

15. Which number should replace the question mark?

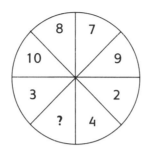

16. Which number should replace the ?

144	4	12	3
180	3	20	3
192	2	24	4
225	5	15	?

17. Find a word which when placed on the end of the first word makes a new word and when placed in front of the second word also makes a new word.

STEAM (. . . .) MATE

18. Find the one-word anagram.

TORN NAME

19. Put in the brackets a word which means the same as the words outside the brackets.

SPRINKLE (. . . . .) BOUQUET

20. Find a 6-letter word made up of these 4 letters only.

JD
RE

21. What is the name given to a group of MAGPIES?

    A TRIP
    B THRONG
    C THICKET
    D TIDING
    E TUFT

22. Find the two words which are SYNONYMS. Both words read clockwise.

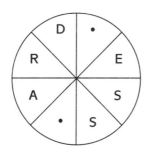 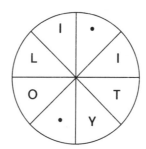

23. Which of these is the odd one out?

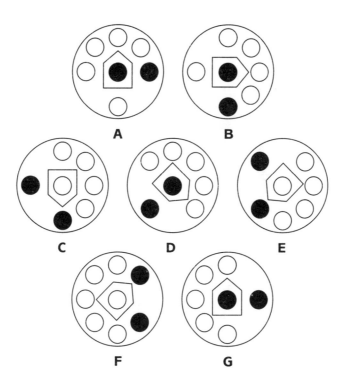

24. Which word in the brackets makes a word when added to the first word and also makes a word when placed in front of the second word.

HAIR (. . . .) AGE

25. Which word means the same as PALATIAL?

regal, flamboyant, largesse, spasmodic, energize

26. HEXAGON
Which hexagon fits the missing space?

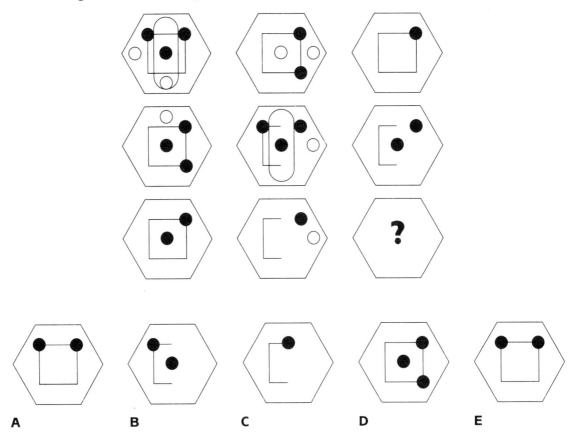

A   B   C   D   E

27. Which number should replace the **?**

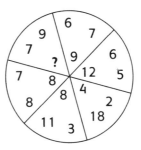

28. Find 3 two-letter bits to equal an 'AN ILLNESS'.

TH   PN   AS   EU   MA   ON

29. Insert a word that means the same as the two words outside the brackets.

THROW (. . . . . .) BOAT

30. SYMBOLS

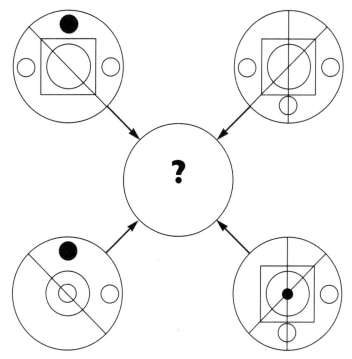

Each line and symbol which appears in the four outer circles above, is transferred to the centre circle according to these rules:

If a line or symbol occurs in the outer circles

once :	it is transferred
twice:	it is possibly transferred
3 times:	it is transferred
4 times:	it is not transferred

Which of the circles A, B, C, D or E shown below should appear at the centre of the diagram above?

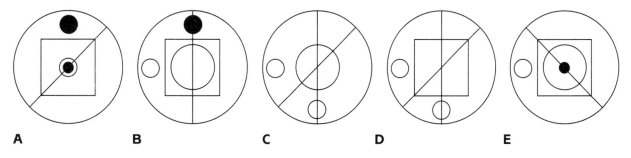

A   B   C   D   E

TEST FOURTEEN

ANSWERS

1. **D** It contains only three small white circles. The rest contain four.
2. Christine
3. 12 Looking across the numbers run +4, −3, +4
   Looking down they run +3, −4, +3
4. **E** cinnabar : red
5. remiss
6. inundate, submerge
7. 18
8. **A** The black dot moves from left to right at each stage. The small white circle moves from right to left.
9. **D** RAN PIPS = parsnip. The fruits are: orange (AN OGRE), apricot (RIP COAT), pumpkin (MINK PUP), mandarin (DAMN RAIN)
10. **E** 3811 : 2628 Reverse and deduct, i.e. 3811 − 1183 = 2628.
11. sieve, colander
12. **B** Only lines common in the first two pentagons are carried forward to the final pentagon and they become curved instead of straight.

13. brae. This is a hill, the rest are valleys.
14. patter
15. 5 Opposite segments total 12.
16. 3 $225 \div (5 \times 15) = 3$
17. SHIP
18. ORNAMENT
19. SPRAY
20. JEERED
21. **D** TIDING
22. HARDNESS, SOLIDITY
23. **F**
24. BAND
25. REGAL
26. **C**
27. 8 $(4 + 18 + 2) = (7 + 9 + 8)$
28. ASTHMA
29. LAUNCH
30. **A**